# GCSE Science for AQA

## Homework and Summary Book

for AQA GCSE A & B and
Additional Applied Science

**Dr Berry Billingsley**
**Gurinder Chadha**
**Katrina Fox**
**Lesley Owen**

G000122757

William Collins' dream of knowledge for all began with the publication of his first book in 1819. A self-educated mill worker, he not only enriched millions of lives, but also founded a flourishing publishing house. Today, staying true to this spirit, Collins books are packed with inspiration, innovation and practical expertise. They place you at the centre of a world of possibility and give you exactly what you need to explore it.

Collins. Freedom to teach.

Published by Collins
An imprint of HarperCollins*Publishers*
77–85 Fulham Palace Road
Hammersmith
London
W6 8JB

Browse the complete Collins catalogue at
www.collinseducation.com

© HarperCollins*Publishers* Limited 2006

10 9 8 7 6 5 4 3 2 1

ISBN-13  978 0 00 721634 5
ISBN-10  0 00 721634 3

The authors assert their moral rights to be identified as the authors of this work.

All rights reserved. No part of this publication may be reproduced, stored in a retrieval system or transmitted in any form or by any means – electronic, mechanical, photocopying, recording or otherwise – without the prior written consent of the Publisher or a licence permitting restricted copying in the United Kingdom issued by the Copyright Licensing Agency Ltd, 90 Tottenham Court Road, London W1T 4LP.

British Library Cataloguing in Publication Data.
A Catalogue record for this publication is available from the British Library.

Commissioned by Cassandra Birmingham

Publishing Manager Michael Cotter

Project managed by Nicola Tidman

Edited by Lynn Watkins

Proofread by Ros Woodward

Cover artwork by Bob Lea

Cover design by Starfish

Internal design and page make-up by JPD

Illustrations by JPD, Peter Harper, Mark Walker, IFADesign Ltd and Peters and Zabransky

Production by Natasha Buckland

Printed and bound by the Bath Press, Glasgow and Bath

**Acknowledgements**
The Publishers gratefully acknowledge the following for permission to reproduce photographs. Whilst every effort has been made to trace the copyright holders, in cases where this has been unsuccessful or if any have been inadvertently overlooked, the Publishers will be pleased to make the necessary arrangements at the first opportunity.

p8 Alfred Pasieka / Science Photo Library; p10 © 2006 JupiterImages Corporation; p11 Michael W. Tweedie / Science Photo Library; p12 Simon Fraser / Science Photo Library; p13 Juz / Science Photo Library; p15 istockphoto; p17 istockphoto; p19 istockphoto; p21 istockphoto; p23 istockphoto, Andrew Lambert Photography / Science Photo Library; p25 istockphoto; p28 istockphoto; p30 istockphoto, © 2006 JupiterImages Corporation; p41 Chemical Design Ltd / Science Photo Library; p43 istockphoto; p48 istockphoto; p49 istockphoto; p50 istockphoto; p54 istockphoto; p55 istockphoto; p56 istockphoto; p63 istockphoto; p65 istockphoto; p66 istockphoto; p68 Bo Veisland / Science Photo Library; p73 Dr P. Marazzi / Science Photo Library; p75 istockphoto; p78 istockphoto; p79 istockphoto

# Contents

## Welcome to Collins GCSE Science!

This Homework and Summary book is designed to help you get the most out of your GCSE Science studies. It covers GCSE Science and Additional Applied, all in one handy book!

There are several sections within the book. Here's how they work.

## Summary content and Now Try This

This book is structured into topics which summarise the content you will learn on your course. The panels of summary points break all of the content down into short handy chunks to help you remember the key ideas. For more details, references to the relevant Collins Science textbook are also provided.

Within each summary panel there is a Now Try This box with practice questions. These questions are provided to help you check your own progress and understanding. Answers are provided at the back of the book.

At the top right of each page you will notice three circles. These are for you to mark in how well you feel you have understood everything on that page. For example:

 I have started this section but I don't completely understand or remember it all yet.

 I am getting better, but I have not yet been able to complete the Now Try This exercises correctly.

 I completely understand this section, and can complete all of the Now Try This exercises correctly.

## Homework questions

Homework questions are provided for every topic. Your teacher will suggest which homework you should do.

## Exam practice

The Exam-style questions pages will let you really prove you understand the Science, and will help you get ready for the exams. Note that these sample exam questions may cover content from more than one topic. This will help keep the key ideas you have learned fresh in your mind.

## Model exam question answers

The Model answers are provided so you can see how questions should be answered.

We hope you find this Homework and Summary book useful. Good luck with your studies!

Your name _____

Class _____

# In control

## THE NERVOUS SYSTEM

- The **central nervous system (CNS)** is made up of the brain and spinal cord.
- **Receptors** in the sense organs detect **stimuli** (changes in the environment).
- **Sensory neurones** carry nerve impulses from receptors to the CNS.
- **Motor neurones** carry impulses from the CNS to **effectors** (muscles or glands).
- Tiny gaps called **synapses** are found where two neurones meet.
- A **reflex action** is a fast, automatic response to a stimulus.

**TOP TIP** Nervous information passes along a neurone as an electrical impulse, but across a synapse as a chemical signal.

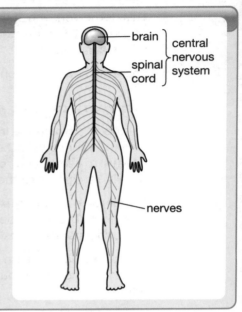

### Homework

1. List the **five** senses and state  a) the organs involved and  b) the receptors they contain.
2. Draw a flow diagram to show how the 'touching a hot object' reflex happens.
3. Describe and explain the different pathways of a reflex action and a conscious action.

## HORMONES

- Keeping conditions inside the body constant is called **homeostasis**.
- **Hormones** are chemical messengers that control and coordinate processes within the body.
- They are secreted by **endocrine glands**.
- They are transported by the bloodstream to their **target organs**.
- Hormones act more slowly than the nervous system and their effects last longer.
- Hormones control things that require constant regulation, such as the levels of sugar and water in the blood, and the menstrual cycle in women.

### Now Try This

a **Complete the passage by filling in the missing words.**

Hormones are _____ messengers that are _____ by endocrine _____.
They travel in the _____ to their _____ organs where they have an effect. Hormonal control is often _____ than nervous control and its effects tend to be _____ lasting.
Hormones control the levels of _____ and _____ in the blood.

### Homework

4. List **three** human glands, the hormones they make and their target organs.
5. Sketch a diagram of the human body, labelling the positions of the following glands: pituitary, pancreas, adrenals, ovaries, testes.
6. State **three** differences between hormonal control and nervous control.

# FERTILITY

- The **menstrual cycle** in women is controlled by the hormones **FSH**, **LH** and **oestrogen**.
- FSH and LH are secreted by the **pituitary gland**.
- FSH:
  - causes eggs to mature in the **ovaries**.
  - stimulates the ovaries to produce oestrogen.
- Oestrogen:
  - inhibits further production of FSH.
  - causes the uterus lining to thicken in preparation for pregnancy.
  - stimulates the pituitary gland to secrete LH.
- LH causes a mature egg to be released from an ovary (**ovulation**).

 **TOP TIP** The menstrual cycle lasts for an average of 28 days. Menstruation begins on day 1 and ovulation occurs at around day 14.

## Now Try This

**b** Write FSH, LH or O (for oestrogen) to answer the following questions.

Which hormone inhibits the production of FSH by the pituitary gland? _____

Which hormone causes the lining of the uterus to thicken? _____

The ovaries are stimulated to produce oestrogen by which hormone? _____

Which hormone causes ovulation to occur? _____

Which hormone is produced by the ovaries? _____

## Homework

7 Explain why oestrogen, used in the oral contraceptive pill, can be used to reduce fertility.

8 Research and write a paragraph on the advantages and disadvantages of the widespread use of oral contraceptives.

9 Explain why FSH can be used to treat infertility.

# DRUGS, ALCOHOL AND TOBACCO

- A **drug** is a chemical that changes the processes in the body.
- Drugs such as **antibiotics** and **painkillers**, can be used to treat medical problems.
- Recreational drugs are used by choice because they make people feel different.
- If a person is **addicted** to a drug they may suffer **withdrawal symptoms** if they stop taking it.
- **Alcohol** can cause slower reactions, loss of self control, unconsciousness and coma. It can damage the brain and liver.
- Tobacco contains several harmful chemicals: **tar** causes cancer, **nicotine** is addictive and **carbon monoxide** reduces the amount of oxygen the blood can carry.
- Smoking tobacco can cause bronchitis, emphysema and lung cancer.

## Now Try This

**c** What do you know about smoking? True (T) or false (F):

Most people take up smoking when they are adults. _____

Pregnant women who smoke have smaller babies. _____

Low-tar cigarettes do not cause lung cancer. _____

Giving up smoking will not reduce the risk of dying from cancer. _____

Smoking relieves stress and so helps to lower blood pressure. _____

You can die from lung cancer even if you don't smoke. _____

## Homework

10 Write a paragraph about why driving under the influence of drugs and alcohol is illegal.

11 Make a list of any legal drugs you can think of and explain how/why they are used.

12 Explain how smoking causes emphysema.

# Keeping healthy

## HEALTHY DIET

- A **balanced diet** contains the correct amounts of **carbohydrates**, **fats**, **proteins**, **vitamins** and **minerals**, **fibre** and **water**.
- **Malnutrition** may lead to deficiency diseases and reduced resistance to infection.
- Lack of exercise and eating too much can lead to **obesity**.
- Too much salt in the diet can lead to high blood pressure (hypertension).
- **Cholesterol** is carried around in the blood as LDL or HDL cholesterol.
- Too much LDL cholesterol can cause heart disease.
- **Saturated fats** increase blood cholesterol levels, contributing to heart disease.

 **TOP TIP** It is the amount of saturated fats eaten, rather than cholesterol, that increases blood cholesterol levels.

### Now Try This

**a** What do you know about eating a healthy diet? Are the following statements true (T) or false (F)?

Heart disease is caused entirely by genetic factors. _____

Cholesterol is an essential component of the diet. _____

Saturated fats are better for you than unsaturated fats. _____

Eating salt can help lower your blood pressure. _____

You do not need to exercise if you are thin. _____

### Homework

1 Use the Internet to find out the recommended daily salt intake. Look at some food packets at home and find out the amount of salt they contain.
2 Give **three** examples of food containing **a)** saturated fats and **b)** unsaturated fats.
3 Write a paragraph to explain the effects of obesity on a person's health.

## BACTERIA AND VIRUSES

- **Bacteria** and **viruses** are **microorganisms**, which reproduce very quickly.
- Bacteria are made of a single cell which is smaller than human cells.
- They can produce **toxins** (poisons) which can make us feel ill.
- Some bacteria are harmless and can actually be useful.
- Viruses are even smaller than bacteria and are not cells.
- Viruses 'hijack' our body's cells and reproduce inside them.
- Viruses burst out of the cells in which they reproduce, killing them.
- Bacteria and viruses that cause disease are called **pathogens**.

### Now Try This

**b** Circle the correct answer.

Bacteria are smaller than:
    human cells    viruses    atoms

Viruses only grow in:
    food    cells    dirty conditions

Bacteria and viruses that cause disease are called:
    microorganisms    pathogens    germs

How many times smaller than bacteria are viruses?
    10    100    about 1000

### Homework

4 List **three** examples of diseases caused by **a)** bacteria and **b)** viruses.
5 List **five** everyday measures you take to avoid being infected by bacteria and viruses.
6 Use the Internet to find **three** uses of bacteria.

## BODY DEFENCES

- The **immune system** attacks and destroys **pathogens** that get inside the body.
- There are two types of **white blood cell**: **phagocytes** and **lymphocytes**.
- Phagocytes ingest ('eat') and digest pathogens to destroy them.

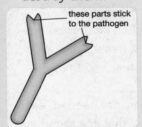
these parts stick to the pathogen

- Lymphocytes produce molecules called **antibodies**, which work against pathogens.
- Antibodies stick to pathogens and disable them so they can be easily attacked by phagocytes.
- **Antibiotics** are drugs that can help treat bacterial infections.
- The shape of a particular antibody means it can only stick to one kind of pathogen, a bit like how a key can only fit one lock.

### Now Try This

**c** Match the following words to their descriptions.

i Bacteria or viruses which cause disease. — phagocytes

ii A molecule produced by lymphocytes. — antibiotic

iii A drug which can be used to treat bacterial infections. — antibody

iv White blood cells that produce antibodies against pathogens. — pathogens

v White blood cells that ingest and destroy pathogens. — lymphocytes

### Homework

7 List **five** ways in which microorganisms can enter your body.

8 Why will your doctor not prescribe antibiotics for a cold or the flu?

9 In your own words, explain how white blood cells fight infection.

## VACCINATION

- **Pathogens** have **antigens** on their surface which **antibodies** stick to.
- An antibody will only stick to one kind of antigen.
- When you are infected, the **lymphocytes** take time to make enough antibodies.
- If you are infected again, the lymphocytes 'remember' the antigen from last time.
- Antibodies are made so quickly that the infection is cleared before you get ill.
- **Vaccines** contain small amounts of dead or disabled pathogen that look the same as the 'real' pathogen but cannot make you ill.
- If you are infected afterwards by the 'real' pathogen, your lymphocytes are ready to make the correct antibody straight away, before you become ill.

 **TOP TIP** Antigens and antibodies have very specific shapes and fit together like a key in a lock.

### Now Try This

**d** Complete the passage by filling in the missing words.

There are two types of white blood cells. Phagocytes _____ ('eat') pathogens and _____ them. Lymphocytes produce molecules called _____ which stick to _____ on the surface of pathogens. After an infection, lymphocytes remember the antigen so if you are infected again antibodies are produced _____ before you get any _____.

### Homework

10 Explain the difference between an antigen and an antibody.

11 Explain why you can only catch chicken pox once.

12 Use the Internet to find out about the risks and benefits of the MMR vaccine.

# Reproduction and genes

## REPRODUCTION

- Individuals need to reproduce to prevent a species from dying out.
- There are two types of **reproduction**: **sexual** and **asexual**.
- Asexual reproduction requires only one parent and produces genetically identical offspring (**clones**).
- Asexual reproduction allows organisms to reproduce very quickly, for example bacteria.
- Sexual reproduction requires two parents.
- **Gametes** (sex cells) from each parent join together (fuse) at **fertilisation**.
- Offspring contain genes from each parent and so show more **variation**.

**TOP TIP** Individuals produced by asexual reproduction may show differences due to environmental factors.

### Now Try This

**a** Complete the passage by filling in the missing words.

_____ reproduction needs just one parent. The offspring are genetically _____ to each other and to the _____. In _____ reproduction, two parents are needed, each producing _____ that join together during _____. The _____ have a mixture of the parents' genetic information and show more _____ than offspring produced asexually.

### Homework

1 Draw a table to compare the features of sexual and asexual reproduction.
2 Use a search engine to find **five** examples of species which reproduce asexually.
3 Two strawberry plants are clones. Why might one be much bigger than the other?

## YOU AND YOUR GENES

- Genetic information is found in the **nucleus** of a cell.
- **Chromosomes** are made up of the chemical **DNA** (deoxyribonucleic acid).
- A **gene** is a section of DNA that 'codes' for a **characteristic**, such as eye colour.
- Human body cells contain 23 pairs of chromosomes (46 in total).
- **Sperm** and **egg cells** each contain a set of 23 individual chromosomes.
- At fertilisation, the two sets of chromosomes combine to give an **embryo** with half of its genes coming from the mother and half from the father.

### Now Try This

**b** Match the following words to their descriptions.

i   The fusion (joining) of two gametes.        nucleus

ii  A sex cell, such as a sperm or an egg.      chromosomes

iii Chemical from which chromosomes are made.   fertilisation

iv  Part of the cell where chromosomes are found.   DNA

v   Structures that contain genes and are found in the nucleus.   gamete

### Homework

4 Explain how fertilisation in humans produces an embryo with 46 chromosomes.
5 Draw a diagram of a human cell, labelling the nucleus, chromosomes and a gene.
6 Make a list of characteristics that are completely determined by your genes.

# GENETIC ENGINEERING

- **Genetic engineering** involves removing **genes** from one species and transferring them into another.
- For example, bacteria have been genetically engineered to produce human **insulin**.
- The insulin gene is first identified and removed from human cells.
- **Restriction enzymes** act like chemical 'scissors' to snip the wanted gene from the rest of the **chromosome**.
- This gene is then attached to chromosomes taken from bacteria.
- The modified chromosomes are put back into the bacteria, which now produce human insulin.
- Genes for **resistance** to pests and weedkillers can be transferred into plant cells by genetic engineering.

 Most diabetics use insulin produced by genetically engineered bacteria. It is cheaper and more effective than animal insulin.

## Now Try This

**c** Put these sentences in the correct order.

☐ Put chromosomes back into bacteria.

☐ Choose the human gene required.

☐ Grow bacteria with the new gene to make insulin.

☐ Attach human gene to bacterial chromosome.

☐ Use restriction enzymes to remove the wanted gene.

## Homework

7 Write a paragraph to explain your views on genetic engineering.

8 Use food labels to make a list of **five** items that contain GM ingredients.

9 Use the Internet to find **two** examples of genetic engineering.

# CLONING

- **Clones** are genetically identical individuals.
- Producing new plants by taking **cuttings** from older plants is an example of cloning.
- **Tissue culture** can be used to take a small group of plant cells and use these to grow a whole new plant.
- In animals, the cells of **embryos** can be divided up to produce several identical embryos which are transplanted into **surrogate** animals.
- In **adult cell cloning**, a nucleus from an egg cell is removed and replaced with the nucleus from an adult cell.
- The resulting individual is identical to the adult from which it was cloned.

 Embryo transplants can be used to help breed endangered species by transplanting the embryos into non-endangered surrogate animals.

## Now Try This

**d** What do you know about cloning? Are the following statements true (T) or false (F)?

Cloning can only be carried out in plants. _____

Cloning produces individuals that are genetically identical. _____

Clones will always look exactly the same as each other. _____

Identical twins are examples of clones. _____

Cloning can be useful. _____

Cloned individuals are always less healthy. _____

## Homework

10 Explain why a breeder of racehorses might want to use embryo transplantation.

11 Write a paragraph to explain your views on adult cell cloning.

12 Why do you think some people are against cloning?

# Evolution and extinction

## ADAPTATION AND SURVIVAL

- Plants and animals require supplies of materials, such as food and oxygen, from their environment in order to survive.
- There are never enough of these materials to go around, so organisms **compete** for the available resources.
- Plants and animals have special features which make them well suited to their environment and more likely to survive.
- **Adaptations** may be behavioural, for example huddling in penguins.
- In cold climates, a small surface area to volume ratio helps animals reduce heat loss.

- In hot climates, cacti reduce water loss by having spines instead of leaves.
- Adaptation allows species to **evolve**, as the best adapted organisms are more likely to survive and reproduce.

### Now Try This

**a** Complete the passage by filling in the missing words.

Adaptations are _____ or _____ which make an organism well _____ to its _____. This makes it more likely that they will _____ and _____.

 **TOP TIP** Surface area to volume ratio is the amount of skin or surface an animal has over its body compared to its body size or volume.

### Homework

1 Describe how a camel is adapted to live in desert conditions.
2 Design an animal to live in a polar environment.
3 Write a paragraph, using examples, to explain what competition is.

## THEORIES OF EVOLUTION

- **Fossils** are the remains of plants and animals that lived millions of years ago.
- Fossils form when dead organisms are buried soon after death for millions of years, preventing decay.
- Similarities between fossils and living species provide evidence for **evolution**.
- Jean-Baptiste Lamarck thought that an organism's environment caused it to change, and that these changes were passed on to offspring.
- Darwin later put forward his theory of evolution by **natural selection**.

 **TOP TIP** Evolution is a process of gradual, continuous change in the characteristics of organisms over long periods of time.

### Now Try This

**b** What do you know about evolution? Are the following statements true (T) or false (F)?

Evolution is still going on today. _____

Most of the species that have ever existed are now extinct. _____

Evolution only occurs in animals. _____

Plants decay and so cannot form fossils. _____

Fossils prove that evolution has occurred. _____

Some people do not believe in evolution. _____

### Homework

4 Write a paragraph to explain how Lamarck accounted for long necks in giraffes.
5 Why is the fossil record incomplete?
6 Explain why Lamarck's theory of evolution is incorrect.

## NATURAL SELECTION

- **Charles Darwin** observed how different species are adapted to their **environments**.
- Individuals differ within populations and some are better **adapted** than others.
- Those that are best adapted are more likely to survive long enough to reproduce.
- They reproduce and pass on the **characteristics** that enable them to survive.
- He called this '**survival of the fittest**'.
- We now know that differences between individuals are due to **genes**, which are passed on to offspring.
- In recent years **natural selection** has caused the evolution of antibiotic-resistant strains of bacteria.

 **TOP TIP** Genetic mutations may create new genes that make organisms more likely to survive.

### Now Try This

c Rearrange the following sentences to describe how natural selection occurs.

  i The genes that helped them survive are passed on to the offspring.

  ii There is variation within a population.

  iii The best adapted individuals survive and reproduce.

  iv Some individuals are better adapted than others.

  v The offspring are well adapted to the environment.

### Homework

7 Write a paragraph to explain how antibiotic resistance arises in bacteria.

8 Why was Darwin's theory not accepted straight away?

9 Explain, using the giraffe as an example, how natural selection occurs.

## EXTINCTION

- If an organism dies out completely it is said to be **extinct**.
- Extinction happens when an organism cannot adapt to its environment.
- If the environment changes significantly there may not be any individuals who can survive.
- A new **disease** or **predator** may kill all organisms in a **population**.
- A new **competitor** may be better adapted to their habitat and out-compete them for vital resources.
- **Habitat** destruction due to human activity may cause the extinction of some **endangered species** in the near future.

 **TOP TIP** Existing diseases and predators do not cause extinction as populations are adapted to these environmental factors.

### Now Try This

d Which of the following are possible causes of extinction?

  i A tsunami which submerges a whole island. ☐

  ii A harsh winter. ☐

  iii Clearing large areas of forest. ☐

  iv Use of pesticides on crops. ☐

  v An outbreak of an existing disease. ☐

  vi An earthquake. ☐

### Homework

10 Describe **two** ways in which humans can contribute to the extinction of a species.

11 Use the Internet to find a list of endangered species.

12 Research and write a paragraph on why the Dodo became extinct.

# Our impact on the environment

## TOO MANY PEOPLE

- The human **population** has risen rapidly over the last 300 years and is still increasing.
- People are living longer as there are fewer deaths from starvation and disease.
- An increased population places greater demands on the Earth's **resources**.
- More land is used for agriculture and building.
- **Fertilisers** and **pesticides** used in agriculture pollute the environment.
- More **waste** is produced and **raw materials** such as **fossil fuels** are being used up.
- Land which was once a **habitat** for plants or animals is no longer available.

### Now Try This

a Complete the passage by filling in the missing words.

The human population is _____. People are living _____ as improved _____ means better food, and better _____ care means fewer deaths from _____. More land is now being used for _____ and _____ and more _____ is being produced.

### Homework

1 Explain why population growth is greater in the developing world.
2 List **three** natural resources that humans are using up.
3 Explain how an increasing population leads to habitat destruction.

## POLLUTION AND ACID RAIN

- **Pollution** is caused by improper handling of waste from human activity.
- Water may be polluted with **sewage** or **fertilisers** from agriculture.
- Air may be polluted with smoke and chemicals from burning fuels.
- Land may be polluted with **pesticides** and **herbicides** from agriculture.
- **Sulfur dioxide** and **oxides of nitrogen** are released from power stations and motor vehicles emit exhaust fumes.
- These gases dissolve in moisture in the air to produce **acid rain**.
- Acid rain damages trees and buildings. It also makes lakes acidic which kills off aquatic life.

 **TOP TIP** Living organisms can be used as indicators of pollution, for example, lichens are sensitive to the amount of sulfur dioxide in the air.

### Now Try This

b Which kind of pollution (air, water, land) do the following cause?

Driving a motor vehicle _____

Using fertilisers in farming _____

Dumping sewage _____

Burning a coal fire _____

Using electricity at home _____

Failing to recycle domestic rubbish _____

Use of pesticides in agriculture _____

### Homework

4 Explain how wasting electricity at home can result in pollution.
5 Write a paragraph about what humans should do to reduce pollution.
6 Make a list of all the things you could do to reduce your contribution to pollution.

# GLOBAL WARMING

- **Carbon dioxide** and **methane** in the atmosphere prevent heat escaping from the Earth's surface.
- Some heat is re-radiated back to the Earth, which keeps it warm.
- This '**greenhouse effect**' maintains a temperature warm enough to sustain life.
- Atmospheric carbon dioxide levels are increasing due to burning **fossil fuels** and **deforestation**.
- An increased greenhouse effect may be causing the Earth's atmosphere to heat up. This is known as **global warming**.
- Global warming may cause climate changes and a rise in sea level.
- Methane produced by herds of cattle and rice fields is also a '**greenhouse gas**'.

**TOP TIP** Deforestation reduces the rate of carbon dioxide use by plants in photosynthesis, and also destroys habitats.

## Now Try This

**c Complete the passage by filling in the missing words.**

Carbon dioxide and methane are examples of _____ gases. They prevent _____ escaping the Earth's surface. Some of this heat is _____ back to Earth. This keeps the Earth's surface _____ than it would otherwise be. An increased _____ effect may be leading to _____ _____. Human activities such as burning _____ _____ and _____ are contributing to this problem.

## Homework

7  Explain the difference between the greenhouse effect and global warming.

8  List **five** things that could be done to reduce global warming.

9  Write a paragraph about the possible effects of global warming.

# SUSTAINABLE DEVELOPMENT

- Improving the quality of life without damaging the environment and compromising future generations is called **sustainable development**.
- This involves reducing pollution and conserving the Earth's resources.
- Sustainable development requires management at local, regional and global levels.
- Measures that can be taken include:
  - **recycling** of resources such as paper, glass and aluminium.
  - use of **renewable energy** resources, such as **wind power** and **solar power**.
  - energy-efficient homes, using insulation and double glazing.
  - reducing the use of motor vehicles by walking, cycling or using public transport.
  - planting a new tree for each tree cut down.
  - quotas on pollution imposed on governments.

**TOP TIP** Most of the electricity you use is generated by a power station that burns fossil fuels!

## Now Try This

**d Are the following energy resources renewable (R) or non-renewable (N)?**

Fossil fuels (coal, oil, gas) _____

Wind turbines _____

Nuclear power _____

Wave power _____

Hydroelectric power _____

Solar power _____

Tidal power _____

## Homework

10  List **five** ways in which you could reduce your energy consumption at home.

11  Make a list of all the rubbish you produce in a day which could be recycled.

12  Explain why sustainable development is difficult to manage at a global level.

# All about atoms

## ATOMS AND ELEMENTS

- All substances are made of **atoms**.
- An **element** has only one type of atom.
- There are about 100 different elements which are all shown in the **periodic table**.
- The **groups** contain elements with similar **properties**.
- Different atoms have different **symbols**. Na is for sodium and Cl is for chlorine.
- An atom has a small **nucleus** at its centre and this is surrounded by **electrons**.

 **TOP TIP** If you have only **one type of atom** present then you have only **one** element.

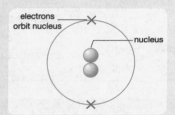
electrons orbit nucleus — nucleus

### Now try this

**a** Match the definition on the left-hand side to the correct word on the right-hand side.

i  Elements are made of one type only.

ii  For calcium it is Ca.

iii  Part of the periodic table where elements have similar properties.

iv  There are about 100 of them.

v  Small central part of atom.

vi  Surround the central nucleus.

nucleus

atom

symbol

group

electrons

elements

### Homework

1  Draw and label a diagram of an atom which contains six protons, six neutrons and six electrons.
2  Use the Internet to find out the origins of **20** element names.
3  See if you can find out which country links the elements yttrium and ytterbium.

## MAKING COMPOUNDS

- A **compound** forms when **elements** react together.
- When a compound forms, this involves the **electrons** from the outer part of the atoms.
- In some cases, different atoms share their electrons to make **chemical bonds**.
- In other cases, bonds are made by atoms giving and taking electrons.
- When chemicals react, no atoms are lost or gained, they are just rearranged.
- We can write **balanced equations** showing the atoms involved in a **chemical reaction**.

 **TOP TIP** We balance equations to show that when chemicals react, no atoms are lost or gained.

### Now try this

**b** Which of these is an element?
$H_2O$    $CO_2$    $CO$    $Co$

**c** Which of these is a compound?
Ca    Ni    NO    H

**d** Which one of these statements is true?
- Atoms are shared when compounds form.
- One type of atom changes to another in chemical reactions.
- Balanced equations show that atoms are not lost or gained in chemical reactions.
- When compounds form this always involves electrons being shared.

### Homework

4  Explain why we must balance chemical equations.
5  What is the difference between an element and a compound?
6  Construct a table to show **five** elements and **five** compounds that can be made from them.

## USING SYMBOLS AND EQUATIONS

- To show what is happening during a chemical reaction we use different symbols, for example + and →.
- The **formula** of a compound shows the number and type of atoms that are joined together to make the compound.
- The formula $Na_2SO_4$ tells us there are two sodium atoms, one sulfur atom and four oxygen atoms in the compound sodium sulfate.
- The equation $2H_2 + O_2 \rightarrow 2H_2O$ tells us that two hydrogen molecules react with one oxygen molecule to make two water molecules.

### Now try this

**e** Complete the following statements.

To show '**reacts with**' we use the symbol _____.

To show '**makes**' we use the symbol _____.

The formula $NaNO_3$ tells us the compound contains _____ sodium atom, _____ nitrogen atom and three _____ atoms.

### Homework

7 Explain what the formula $NH_4NO_3$ tells us.

8 Explain what the formula $Ca(OH)_2$ tells us.

9 Explain what the equation $H_2 + Cl_2 \rightarrow 2HCl$ tells us.

## LIMESTONE

- Limestone contains the compound calcium carbonate.
- Calcium carbonate has the formula $CaCO_3$.
- Limestone is quarried and can be used as a building material.
- Calcium carbonate can be decomposed by heating it. This process is known as thermal decomposition.
- When it decomposes, calcium carbonate makes calcium oxide (quicklime) and carbon dioxide.
- Limestone and its products have many uses, including making slaked lime (calcium hydroxide), mortar, cement, concrete and glass.

*Quarrying limestone*

### Now try this

**f** Look at the following statements and write **T** if they are **true** and **F** if they are **false**. If you think a statement is false then say why you think it is wrong.

| Statement | T or F | If false, why is it wrong? |
|---|---|---|
| i Calcium carbonate contains one calcium atom, one carbon atom and three oxygen atoms. | | |
| ii Limestone is quarried as it has few uses. | | |
| iii Limestone can be made using glass. | | |
| iv Limestone's common name is quicklime. | | |

### Homework

10 Limestone is mainly calcium carbonate. What other rocks are made of calcium carbonate?

11 Investigate other uses of limestone apart from those shown above. How many can you find?

12 Use the Internet to find out **two** counties in Britain where limestone can be quarried.

# Metals from ores

## ORES

- An **ore** contains enough **metal** to make money from extracting the metal.
- An ore which it is not currently **economical** to exploit may become useful if the metal becomes more scarce.
- We can find **unreactive** metals such as **gold** in the Earth, in the form of the metal itself.
- Most metals are found combined with other elements and chemical reactions are needed to extract these metals.
- Low reactivity metals, such as **iron**, can be **extracted** by heating their oxides with carbon.
- Iron oxide can be reduced to iron in a **blast furnace** when carbon takes the oxygen away from the iron.

 Metals lower than carbon in the reactivity series can be extracted from their ores by heating with carbon.

### Now try this

**a** Match the definition on the left-hand side to the correct word on the right-hand side.

  **i** A metal that can be found uncombined in the Earth.      iron oxide

  **ii** A metal usually found combined in the Earth.      ore

  **iii** A non-metal often used to extract metal.      carbon

  **iv** A compound that is used in a blast furnace.      gold

  **v** A rock that contains enough metal to extract and make money.      iron

## Homework

1. Explain in your own words what an ore is.
2. Look on the Internet for a diagram of a blast furnace and label it to show how it works.
3. Name **three** metals that can be found uncombined in the Earth's crust.

## IRON AND ITS ALLOYS

- **Iron** from the **blast furnace** contains 4 % impurities, which makes it **brittle**.
- Removing the impurities produces pure iron, which can be bent and shaped easily.
- In metals such as iron, the atoms are arranged in layers which can slide over each other. This is why these metals can bend.
- Most iron is converted into **steel**, an **alloy** of iron, which contains carbon and other metals.
- Adding different atoms to iron distorts the layers and makes it harder for them to slide over each other. This makes the alloys stronger and harder than pure iron.
- **Low carbon steels** bend easily. **High carbon steel** is very hard. **Stainless steel** does not rust.

 An alloy is a mixture of metals.

### Now try this

**b** Complete the following sentences by filling in the missing words.

Iron from the blast furnace which is only _____ % pure is very _____. When impurities are removed, the pure iron is very _____. Small amounts of carbon may be added to iron to make the _____ low carbon steel. This alloy can easily be bent and shaped. High carbon steels are much _____. Another useful alloy of iron is stainless steel, which does not _____.

## Homework

4. Use the Internet to find out the composition of some alloys of iron.
5. Draw a diagram to show why iron becomes harder when carbon is added.
6. Use the Internet to find out why the Sheffield United football team are called 'The Blades'.

# THE TRANSITION OF METALS

- The elements in the central block of the periodic table (for example, nickel, iron, titanium, copper, gold and silver) are the **transition metals**.
- Like most metals, they are strong and can be bent and hammered into shape.
- This makes them useful for making structures such as bridges.
- Like most metals they are also good **conductors** of heat and electricity.
- **Copper** is used for wiring and plumbing.
- Copper is usually extracted using **electrolysis**.
- Copper ores are not plentiful and low grade ores (not useful previously) are now being exploited commercially.
- The impact on the environment is reduced as there is less new mining.

*Copper piping.*

## Now try this

**c** Circle the correct answer in each group of four.

**i** A transition metal

    titanium    aluminium

    sodium    magnesium

**ii** A property of metals

    brittle    bend

    insulate    don't corrode

**iii** Copper isn't used for making …

    wiring    pipes

    bridges

    plumbing fittings

## Homework

7  Make an illustrated poster all about copper.

8  Find out where copper mines are or have been in Britain.

9  Find out which Mediterranean island gives copper its name, using an online periodic table.

# OTHER ALLOYS

- Pure gold, aluminium and copper are too soft for many uses, so they are made into **alloys** by mixing them with similar metals.
- Some alloys are known as **smart alloys** and these regain their shape after they have been bent, squashed or twisted.
- **Aluminium** is a very useful metal (especially when alloyed) as it has a **low density** and does not rust.
- **Titanium** is another lightweight metal which resists **corrosion**.
- Aluminium and titanium cannot be extracted by heating with carbon.
- Lots of energy and many chemical processes are therefore needed to extract these metals.
- This means that these metals are expensive and, like many metals, it is economical and environmentally friendly to **recycle** them.

## Now try this

**d** Say whether these statements are true or false in the second column. If false, explain why in the third column.

| Statement | T or F | If false, why is it wrong? |
|---|---|---|
| **i** Smart alloys have shape memory. | | |
| **ii** Titanium has a low density but corrodes. | | |
| **iii** Pure gold is too hard for many uses. | | |
| **iv** Aluminium is recycled as it is expensive to extract. | | |
| **v** Aluminium is expensive as it is a limited resource. | | |

## Homework

10  Find out about a smart alloy and write about it in your own words.

11  Explain why titanium and aluminium are such useful metals.

12  List as many uses for aluminium as you can.

# Crude oil

## CRUDE OIL IS A MIXTURE

- **Crude oil** is a **mixture** containing many different compounds.
- In a mixture, the **elements** or **compounds** are not chemically combined with each other.
- The components of a mixture can be separated using the physical differences between them.
- Each of the components of a mixture keeps its own properties.
- The different compounds in crude oil can be separated by **fractional distillation**.

 **TOP TIP** Fractional distillation works because the different compounds in crude oil have different boiling points.

### Now try this

**a** Complete the following sentences by filling in the missing words.

Crude oil is a _____ of different _____. The different compounds can be separated using _____ _____ because each of the compounds has a different _____ _____.

## Homework

1. Use examples to explain the differences between a mixture, a compound and an element.
2. Construct a table that shows **three** examples of a mixture, a compound and an element.
3. Explain why fractional distillation is able to separate out the components of crude oil.

## ALKANES

- Most of the **compounds** in **crude oil** are compounds called **hydrocarbons**.
- A hydrocarbon is a compound made only of the elements **hydrogen** and **carbon**.
- Most of the hydrocarbons in crude oil are **saturated** hydrocarbons.
- These saturated hydrocarbons are called **alkanes**.
- Alkanes have the general formula $C_nH_{2n+2}$.
- Alkane molecules can be shown in the following ways:

### Now try this

**b** Circle the correct answer.

**i** Alkanes are

    compounds   mixtures   elements

**ii** Alkanes have the general formula

    $C_{2n}+2H_n$   $C_nH_{2n+2}$   $C_nH_{2n}$

**iii** Alkanes are

    unsaturated   saturated   saturation

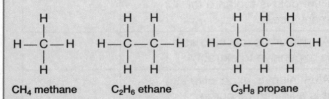

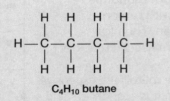

$CH_4$ methane    $C_2H_6$ ethane    $C_3H_8$ propane    $C_4H_{10}$ butane

 **TOP TIP** In an alkane every carbon atom must have four single bonds.

## Homework

4. What do you understand by the term hydrocarbon?
5. What name is given to a hydrocarbon with four carbons in it?
6. Work out the formula of an alkane with 22 carbons in it.

# FRACTIONAL DISTILLATION OF CRUDE OIL

- **Crude oil** can be separated into **fractions** by **fractional distillation**.
- Each fraction is still a mixture, but the compounds in each fraction have a similar number of carbons.
- To separate crude oil it is first heated.
- This makes the compounds evaporate.
- The gases are then allowed to cool and they condense at different temperatures.
- The way molecules behave depends on their size.
- The size of a molecule determines whether or not it will be a good fuel.

## Now try this

**c** Number the list correctly so that it is in the right order to show fractional distillation.

☐ The gases are cooled.

☐ You end up with different fractions containing similar numbers of molecules.

☐ This evaporates all of the compounds.

☐ Crude oil is heated.

☐ The different molecules condense at different temperatures.

## Homework

7  Make a poster and illustrate it to show how fractional distillation works.

8  Explain what is meant by the term 'fraction'.

9  Use the Internet to find out what 'Brent Crude' is.

# WHAT FORMS WHEN FUELS BURN?

- Most **fuels** contain carbon and/or hydrogen.
- When these fuels burn, the carbon forms carbon dioxide, $CO_2$ (which causes **global warming**) and the hydrogen forms water vapour, $H_2O$.
- Sometimes **solid particles** form and these cause **global dimming**.
- Some fuels contain sulfur (S), as an impurity. In vehicle fuels the sulfur is removed before the fuel is burnt.
- If not removed, these fuels release **sulfur dioxide** ($SO_2$) as well as $CO_2$ and $H_2O$.
- Sulfur dioxide causes **acid rain**. In power stations, it must be removed from the gases before they leave the chimney.

## Now try this

**d** Answer these questions using one of the following answers: S, $CO_2$, $SO_2$, $H_2O$, solid particles.

The two gases made when a hydrocarbon burns: _____

The gas that causes acid rain: _____

The gas that must be removed from power stations after fuels are burnt: _____

The substance present as an impurity in some hydrocarbon fuels: _____

The gas made when hydrogen fuel burns: _____

The gas made when carbon burns: _____

The substance that causes global dimming: _____

## Homework

10  Make a poster to show how all the pollutants mentioned above are formed.

11  Which pollutant causes global dimming?

12  Find out how sulfur dioxide is removed from power station chimneys.

# Cracking and polymers

## CRACKING HYDROCARBONS

- As a result of **fractional distillation** we end up with too many of the larger molecules and not enough of the smaller molecules.
- The large molecules can be 'cracked' to break them into smaller, more useful molecules. This is known as **thermal decomposition**.
- Cracking involves passing the heated vapours of large molecules over a hot **catalyst**.
- Cracking always makes smaller **alkanes** and **alkenes**.
- Alkenes are **unsaturated hydrocarbons** with the general formula $C_nH_{2n}$.
- Alkenes can be shown as: $C_3H_6$ or

**TOP TIP** Cracking always makes at least one alkene and an alkane.

### Now try this

a Circle the correct answer.

i Cracking does not need
    heat    a catalyst    small hydrocarbons

ii Alkenes have the general formula
    $C_nH_n$    $C_{2n}H_n$    $C_nH_{2n}$

iii An example of an alkene is
    $C_4H_{10}$    $C_7H_{14}$    $C_2H_2$

iv Alkenes are not
    molecules    hydrocarbons    saturated

v The structural formula of propene is

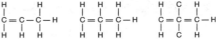

vi Cracking makes
    big molecules    small molecules    crude oil

### Homework

1 Draw a flow chart to show how propene ($C_3H_6$) is obtained from crude oil.

2 Explain why cracking is useful.

3 Draw a diagram to show a molecule of butene, $C_4H_8$.

## USING THE PRODUCTS OF CRACKING

- Some of the products that are made from **cracking** are used as **fuels**.
- This is because cracking makes more of the smaller molecules that burn well.
- **Ethene** ($C_2H_4$) reacts with steam ($H_2O$) in the presence of a **catalyst** to make **ethanol**.
- Good quality ethanol can be made quickly by this method.
- Making ethanol in this way (as opposed to making it from fermenting sugar) means a non-renewable source is being used.
- **Alkenes** can be used to make **polymers** such as poly(ethene) and poly(propene).

### Now try this

b Complete the sentences by filling in the missing words.

Alkenes react with _____ in the presence of a _____ to make compounds called alcohols. For example, _____ can be reacted with _____ in the presence of a catalyst to make ethanol. Alkenes are also useful because they can be used to make _____ such as _____ and poly(propene). As well as making alkenes, cracking also makes smaller _____, which can be used as _____.

### Homework

4 How is ethanol made from ethene?

5 Why is making ethanol by this method better than making it by fermentation?

6 Why is making ethanol by this method not as good as making it by fermentation?

# FROM MONOMER TO POLYMER

- In order to make a **polymer** the **monomer** must have a **double bond**. It must be **unsaturated**.
- When a small molecule such as **ethene** is used to make poly(ethene) we say that ethene is a monomer.
- When many thousands of monomers are added together, a polymer is made.
- When many thousands of ethene monomers are reacted together, the polymer poly(ethene) forms.
- When many thousands of propene monomers are reacted together, the polymer poly(propene) forms.

## Now try this

**c** Link the monomer to the polymer.

| | |
|---|---|
| **i** ethene | poly(propene) |
| **ii** $C_3H_6$ | poly(styrene) |
| **iii** styrene | poly(butene) |
| **iv** $C_4H_8$ | poly(ethene) |

## Homework

7 Explain why $C_2H_6$ cannot be used to make polymers.

8 Draw a cartoon, a picture or make a model to show how polymers form.

9 Use the Internet to find the monomer that is used to make PVC.

# PROPERTIES AND USES OF POLYMERS

- The way in which a particular **polymer** behaves depends on what the **monomer** is and the conditions it was made under.
- Slime can be made from the polymer poly(ethenol), which is also known as PVA. The **viscosity** (how easily it flows) can be varied according to the conditions it is made under.
- Polymers have many uses including: packaging materials, waterproof fabric coatings, dental polymers for fillings, dressings for wounds and hydrogels.
- **Smart materials** such as 'shape memory plastics' are also being developed.
- There are so many **plastics** now in use that disposal has become a problem.
- It is desirable to **recycle** plastics but they are difficult to separate from each other before recycling.
- We can dispose of polymers by burning them but some may release toxic fumes.
- Polymers are not **biodegradable** and therefore **landfill sites** are not a solution to the problem of disposal.

## Now try this

**d** Say whether you think these statements are true or false. If a statement is false, explain why.

| Statement | T or F | If false, why is it wrong? |
|---|---|---|
| **i** Plastics are easy to recycle. | | |
| **ii** Plastics are finding more and more uses. | | |
| **iii** A good way to dispose of plastics is to burn them. | | |
| **iv** Plastics cannot be broken down by bacteria. | | |

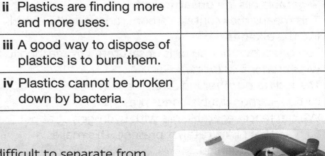

## Homework

10 Bring in **three** different polymers from home and add them to a collection at school.

11 Explain why disposing of polymers is such a problem.

12 Use the Internet to find out why 'shape memory plastics' are clever and write about them.

# Food chemistry

## PLANT OILS

- Many of the oils we use are **extracted** from nuts, seeds and fruits.
- To extract the oil, the plant material is crushed to squeeze it out. In some cases the oil is separated off by **distillation**. Water and impurities are removed.
- Vegetable oils are useful fuels and foods as they contain a lot of **energy**.
- Oils are a useful part of our diet as they provide us with **nutrients**.
- Oils do not dissolve in water, but we can make them mix by turning them into **emulsions**.
- Emulsions are thicker than either the oil or water on their own and they have better texture, appearance and ability to coat.
- Two emulsions you know of are salad dressing and ice cream.

### Now try this

**a** **Complete the sentences by filling in the missing words.**

Plant oils are useful in our diet as they provide _____ and _____. Oil and vinegar will not mix so we add an emulsifier such as _____ to make them join together and form an _____. Salad dressing is better than oil and vinegar separately because it can _____ the food more easily and has a thicker _____.

### Homework

1 Go home and ask your parents what different types of oil they use in the kitchen.
2 Try to make an emulsion at home using vinegar and oil. Try different emulsifiers.
3 Write a report of your experiment.

## SATURATED OR UNSATURATED?

- Vegetable oils are **unsaturated**.
- This means they contain carbon–carbon double bonds like the **alkenes**.
- You can show that an oil is unsaturated by reacting it with bromine or iodine.
- The **iodine number** indicates the number of carbon–carbon double bonds present.
- We can react vegetable oils with hydrogen at about 60 °C with a nickel catalyst present. This makes a **hard fat** (margarine).
- The hardened oils have higher melting points so they are solids at room temperature. This means they can be spread on foods and are easier to use for cake-making.

 **TOP TIP** To test for unsaturation just add bromine or iodine solution and if they lose their colour, you know there were double bonds present.

### Now try this

**b** **Match the statements on the right-hand side with the type of hydrocarbon.**

|  |  |
|---|---|
|  | methane |
|  | $C_3H_6$ |
| unsaturated | decolourises bromine |
|  | iodine solution stays brown |
|  | $C_3H_8$ |
|  | contains only C–C single bonds |
| saturated | contains at least one C–C double bond |
|  | general formula is $C_nH_{2n}$ |

### Homework

4 How do you make margarine from vegetable oils?
5 What is meant by a catalyst?
6 Explain the benefits of hardening oils.

# FOOD ADDITIVES

- **Additives** may be added to make food stay fresh for longer.
- Additives may be added to improve the appearance or taste of a food.
- Additives must be listed with the ingredients.
- Some additives have **E-numbers**.
- The presence of additives can be identified using **chemical analysis**.
- We can identify added (or natural) colours using **chromatography**.
- To obtain a chromatogram like the one below, you draw a pencil line near the bottom of the chromatography paper. Place a few drops of an **extract** from each food sample on the line and then dip the paper in some **solvent** in a beaker.

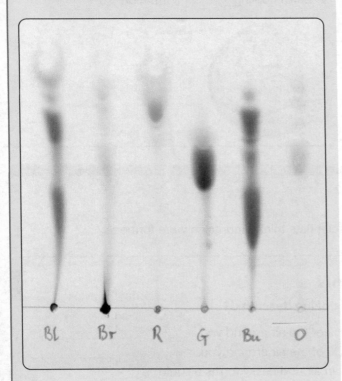

## Now try this

**c** The chromatogram shown below has been made to analyse colours used in frozen peas. Six samples were tested. Look at the chromatogram and answer the questions that follow.

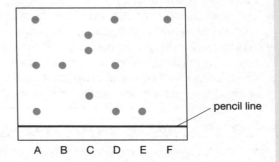

pencil line

A  B  C  D  E  F

**i** Which samples contained at least **three** different dyes? _____

**ii** Which samples probably contained only a single dye? _____

**iii** Which samples contained the same dye as in B? _____

**iv** Which sample contained different dyes from all of the rest? _____

**TOP TIP** Once you understand how to 'read' this chromatogram you should be able to understand any other chromatogram.

## Homework

7 Find the names of **five** different food additives by reading labels on food in your kitchen.

8 Use the Internet to find out what is so bad about the food additive E-102.

9 Use the information you have found to make an information leaflet about additive E-102.

# The Earth and its atmosphere

## THE EARTH'S CRUST

- Scientists used to think that the Earth's surface features were due to uneven shrinking of the Earth as it cooled down following its formation.
- We now know that ideas about **tectonic plates** explain the presence of some of the Earth's physical features, for example, mountains and oceans.
- The top part of the Earth (the **crust** and top part of the **mantle**) is broken into large pieces called tectonic plates.
- These plates move at speeds of several centimetres a year.
- They move because they lie above **convection currents** in the mantle.
- The heat that causes convection in the mantle comes from **radioactive decay** processes.
- The movements can, at times, be sudden and may cause disasters such as **earthquakes**.
- Earthquakes and **volcanic eruptions** occur along the edges of plates where they meet.

### Now try this

**a** Match the descriptions on the right-hand side with the words on the left-hand side.

| | | |
|---|---|---|
| **i** | tectonic plate | a few metres every century |
| | | occur at plate boundaries |
| **ii** | radioactive decay | provides energy for convection currents in the mantle |
| **iii** | plate movement | |
| | | large piece of Earth's crust and upper mantle |
| **iv** | volcanoes | |
| | | has occurred since its formation |
| **v** | Earth cooling | |

thin rocky crust

mantle

core with liquid outer part and solid inner part

## Homework

1 Which layers of the Earth form tectonic plates?
2 What causes tectonic plates to move?
3 Before the theory of plate tectonics, how did scientists think mountains were formed?

## THE EARTH'S ATMOSPHERE

- The **atmosphere** today has been much the same for the last 200 million years.
- It contains about 80% **nitrogen**.
- It contains about 20% oxygen.
- There are small amounts of other gases including **water vapour**, **carbon dioxide** and **noble gases** (mainly **argon**).

### Now try this

**b** Which gas is being described?

i Forms 80% of the air around you. _____

ii Forms 20% of the air around you. _____

iii Is present in air and easily forms a liquid on cooling. _____

iv Present in air in tiny amounts and we exhale it. _____

v The amount in air depends on the temperature. _____

## Homework

4 Draw a pie chart to show the composition of the Earth's atmosphere.
5 Find uses for all the gases in your pie chart.
6 Why is it that lots of people don't know that nitrogen is in the air?

## USES OF NOBLE GASES

- The **noble gases** are in **group 0** of the **periodic table**.
- The noble gases are extremely **unreactive**.
- Noble gases can be used in light bulbs (filament lamps) and discharge lamps, like neon lights and strip lights.
- **Helium**, another noble gas, is much less dense than air and can be used in balloons.

### Now try this

c Which gas is being described?

i Can be used in discharge tubes. _____

ii A noble gas not used in balloons. _____

iii The lightest noble gas. _____

 **TOP TIP** The use of noble gases depends on the fact that they are not very reactive.

### Homework

7 Make an information poster or PowerPoint show about the noble gases.

8 Find out why the noble gases are so unreactive.

9 Some metals are known as 'Noble Metals'. Use the Internet to find out their names.

## HOW THE EARTH'S ATMOSPHERE DEVELOPED

- For the first billion years on Earth, there was powerful **volcanic activity** at the surface.
- This released the gases which formed the Earth's early atmosphere.
- The main gas present was **carbon dioxide** ($CO_2$) and there was no **oxygen** ($O_2$).
- This is like the atmosphere of Venus and Mars today.
- It is thought that the other gases were **water vapour** ($H_2O$), small amounts of **ammonia** ($NH_3$) and **methane** ($CH_4$).
- As the surface cooled, the water vapour condensed to make the oceans.
- Oxygen only appeared in our atmosphere after plants evolved.
- Carbon dioxide was removed as it became locked up in **sedimentary carbonate rocks** (such as limestone and chalk) and **fossil fuels** (such as oil and coal).
- Recently we have started to release this carbon dioxide by burning large amounts of fossil fuels.

*Carbon dioxide locked up millions of years ago is released when we burn this coal.*

### Now try this

d Answer **UP** or **DOWN** to each of these questions.

Formation of fossil fuels makes $CO_2$ levels in the atmosphere go _____

Formation of chalk makes $CO_2$ levels in the atmosphere go _____

Evolution of plants made the amount of $O_2$ in the atmosphere go _____

Burning fossil fuels makes $CO_2$ levels in the atmosphere go _____

Condensation of $H_2O$ makes levels of this gas in the atmosphere go _____

Since the first billion years of the Earth's existence, $CO_2$ levels have gone _____

Since the first billion years of the Earth's existence, $NH_3$ levels have gone _____

Since the first billion years of the Earth's existence, volcanic activity has gone _____

Global warming would make the level of water vapour in the atmosphere go _____

### Homework

10 Which gases were present in the Earth's early atmosphere?

11 Where has all the $CO_2$ from the Earth's early atmosphere gone?

12 Why is the amount of $CO_2$ in the atmosphere increasing nowadays?

# Thermal energy

## THERMAL RADIATION

### Now try this

**a** Which of the following statements are true?

  **i** Thermal radiation is emitted by rays known as infrared waves. _____

  **ii** A red-hot oven emits more thermal radiation than when it is cold. _____

  **iii** Polar bears absorb lots of thermal radiation because of their white fur. _____

  **iv** An object at –20 °C is warmer than an object at –50 °C. _____

 **TOP TIP** All bodies emit and absorb thermal radiation.

- **Temperature** is measured with a **thermometer** in **degrees Celsius** (°C).
- The temperature of a body is a measure of its 'hotness'.
- **Energy** can be transferred by **conduction**, **convection** and **radiation**.
- **Thermal radiation** is the transfer of energy by **electromagnetic waves** known as **infrared waves**.
- The infrared radiation emitted by an object (for example, a person) can be detected by a 'thermal imaging camera' or a thermopile.
- The hotter a body is the more energy it radiates as thermal radiation.
- The greater the temperature difference between a body and its surroundings, the greater the rate at which energy is transferred.
- Dark, matt surfaces are good **absorbers** and good **emitters** of thermal radiation.
- Shiny surfaces **reflect** infrared radiation.
- Light, shiny surfaces are poor absorbers and poor emitters of thermal radiation.
- Infrared radiation does not require a medium.

## Homework

1. In your own words, describe the difference between temperature and heat.
2. Make a list of objects emitting infrared radiation in your house.
3. Write a short paragraph on the properties of infrared radiation as an electromagnetic wave.

# CONVECTION

- In **convection**, energy transfer occurs due to the movement of a **fluid** (liquid or gas).
- Convection can only happen in fluids (liquids and gases) where the atoms or particles are free to move.
- In convection, hot liquid (or air) rises and is replaced by falling colder liquid (or air). This gives rise to **convection currents**.

## Now try this

**b** Which of the following statements is/are correct?

i Metals cannot transfer heat by convection because the particles cannot move. _____

ii Convection is not possible in a vacuum because there are no particles. _____

iii Convection is impossible in water. _____

## Homework

4 Use a labelled diagram to explain how convection currents are set up in a kettle full of water.

5 Describe how a 'radiator' at one end of a room heats the air in that room.

6 Make a list of examples of convection currents.

# CONDUCTION

- Good **thermal conductors** allow easy transfer of heat energy.
- Poor thermal conductors are known as **insulators**, for example glass and plastic.
- In a solid, thermal energy is transferred by atomic or particle **vibrations**.
- **Metals** are good thermal conductors because the energy is transferred by both atomic vibrations and by free electrons.
- The transfer of energy by the free electrons is faster than by atomic vibrations.
- **Non-metals** (for example, plastic, wood) are poor thermal conductors because they have fewer free electrons.
- **Liquids** (for example, water) and **gases** (for example, air) are poor thermal conductors or good thermal insulators.
- Many insulators in the home contain trapped air (for example, loft insulation or fibreglass, double glazing in windows and cavity-wall insulation foam).
- A **vacuum** is a perfect insulator because there are no particles.

## Now try this

**c** Cross out the incorrect word in each statement, leaving the correct word.

i Air is a good **conductor/insulator**.

ii Water is a **poor/good** thermal conductor.

iii Solids are good conductors of heat because the particles are **close together/far apart**.

 Good thermal insulators are poor thermal conductors.

## Homework

7 Make a table of materials under the headings 'good insulators' and 'good conductors'.

8 In your own words, explain why metals are better thermal conductors than non-metals like plastic.

9 Make a list of insulators in your home that minimise the loss of heat.

# Efficient use of energy

## ENERGY

- Some examples of energy:
  - **heat** energy
  - **chemical** energy
  - **electrical** energy
  - **light** energy
  - **wave** energy
  - **sound** energy
  - **nuclear** energy
  - **kinetic** energy
  - **potential** (stored) energy.
- **Conservation** of energy:
  Energy cannot be created or destroyed. The total energy always remains the same.
- Energy can only be **transformed** from one form to another. For example, a light bulb changes electrical energy into light energy and heat energy.

- The energy not used by a device is known as 'wasted energy'.
- The wasted energy is often **transferred** to the surroundings as heat energy.
- The kinetic energy of the atoms increases when heat energy is transferred to the surroundings.
- input energy = wasted energy + useful energy
- Having loft insulation, cavity-wall insulation, double glazing and draught proofing can reduce energy losses from homes.

### Now try this

**a** Complete the sentences.

The useful energy for a car is its
k_____ energy. This
energy comes from the
c_____ energy of the fuel.
Almost half of the input energy
from the fuel is wasted as
h_____ in the moving
parts of the car as exhaust gases.

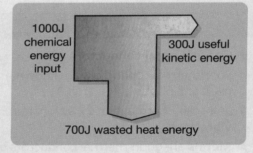

*A Sankey diagram for a car.*

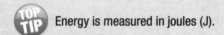 Energy is measured in joules (J).

## Homework

1. Draw a mind map for 'energy'.
2. In your own words, state the principle of conservation of energy and give examples.
3. Give **five** examples of transformation of energy by devices.

# ENERGY, WORK AND POWER

- **Work done** is measured in **joules** (J).
- work done = force × distance moved in the direction of the force
- **energy transfer** = work done
- **Power** is measured in **watts** (W).
- power = $\dfrac{\text{work done}}{\text{time}}$  or  power = $\dfrac{\text{energy transfer}}{\text{time}}$
- One watt is equal to one joule per second.
- A power of 60 W means 60 J of work done per second.

 Energy and work are both measured in joules (J).

### Now try this

**b** Match the beginnings and endings to make complete sentences.

| Beginning | Ending |
|---|---|
| i No work is done on an object if it | second. |
| ii Power is measured in | joules. |
| iii Work is measured in | watts. |
| iv 100 W means 100 J of energy transferred every | remains stationary. |

## Homework

4 Make a list of the typical power rating of the devices in your home, for example, TV or lamp.

5 Use the Internet to research and write about the energy available from some named chocolate bars.

6 Make a list of all the quantities and their units.

# EFFICIENCY

- **efficiency** = $\dfrac{\text{useful energy transferred by device}}{\text{total energy supplied to the device}}$
- The efficiency of a device can be written as a percentage.
- For example, a crane lifts a large tank of water. The total chemical energy supplied to the engine of the crane is 200 000 J. The final potential energy of the water tank is 80 000 J. What is the efficiency of the engine?

  efficiency = $\dfrac{80\,000}{200\,000}$ = 0.40

  efficiency = 0.40 × 100 = 40 %

  60 % of the **input energy** is wasted energy (most likely as heat energy).

- A device is more efficient when a greater percentage of the energy is usefully transformed by the device.

### Now try this

**c** Which of the following statements is/are correct?

i Efficiency has no units. ☐

ii For a car that is 30% efficient, 70% of the energy is wasted. ☐

iii The input electrical energy to a lamp is 100 J. Only 2 J is emitted as light. The efficiency of the lamp is 98%. ☐

 Nothing can be more than 100% efficient.

## Homework

7 In your own words explain why a device with moving parts can never be 100% efficient.

8 Use the energy transfer diagrams given on pages 216 and 217 of the student book to calculate the efficiency of each device.

9 Use the Internet to research the typical efficiencies of modern cars.

# Electricity

## ELECTRICAL DEVICES ARE USEFUL

- Mains **electricity** is convenient and reliable for our domestic appliances.
- Many devices transform **electrical energy** into other forms, for example, heat, light and sound.
- An electric kettle changes electrical energy into heat energy.
- A hairdryer changes electrical energy into kinetic energy and heat energy.
- A TV changes electrical energy into heat energy, light energy and sound energy.
- **Batteries** allow electrical devices to be portable.
- **Solar energy** and **potential energy** in clockwork springs can be used to charge **rechargeable** batteries.
- An electric current in a device causes heating.
- Large **currents** can cause excessive heating that can lead to accidental fires.

### Now try this

**a** Cross out the incorrect word in each statement, leaving the correct word.

A battery changes chemical energy into **heat/electrical** energy.

A filament lamp transforms electrical energy into heat energy and **chemical/light** energy.

A current in the filament lamp makes it **cold/hot**.

A battery-powered torch is convenient because it is **portable/heavy**.

## Homework

1 Write a paragraph on the advantages of using rechargeable batteries in developing countries.
2 Write a paragraph on the advantages and disadvantages of using a mains operated electric power drill.
3 Make a list of items that use batteries.

# COST OF ELECTRICITY

- **Power** is often measured in **watts** (W) or **joules per second** (J/s).
- **Electrical power** is defined as the rate of transfer of electrical energy.
- power = $\dfrac{\text{energy transferred}}{\text{time taken}}$
- The electrical energy **transformed** by a device depends on how long it is used for and the **power rating** of the device.
- energy transferred in joules = power in watts × time in seconds
- The **kilowatt hour** (kWh) is a convenient unit of electrical energy.
- 1 kWh is the energy transferred by a 1 kW device working for a time of 1 hour.
- 1 kWh = 3 600 000 J
- electrical energy transformed in kWh = power in kW × time in hours
- The cost of electricity is calculated using the equation:
  cost = power in kW × time in hours × cost of 1 kWh

## Now try this

**b** Which of the following statements is/are correct?

i The joule is a unit of energy. ☐

ii The kilowatt hour is a unit of energy. ☐

iii The watt is a unit of energy. ☐

iv Using an appliance for longer will cost more. ☐

 **TOP TIP** Do not forget that the kWh is a unit of energy.

## Homework

4 Explain what is meant by the 'joule' and the 'kilowatt hour'. Explain why it is convenient to use the kWh for domestic billing.

5 Make a list of all the quantities in this section and the appropriate units.

6 Estimate the cost of using your electric kettle during a day.

# THE NATIONAL GRID

- The **National Grid** uses transmission cables to distribute electricity between power stations and our homes and factories.
- In a **power station**, **fossil fuel** is burned to heat water in order to produce high-pressured steam. The steam is used to spin **turbines**. The turbines turn the **generators** and this produces **electricity**.
- The **voltage (potential difference)** from the generator is increased from 25 kV to about 400 kV using **step-up transformers**.
- Electricity is transmitted at high voltage to reduce **current** in the cables and hence reduce the energy losses in the transmission cables.
- Before the electricity can be used at our homes it has to be decreased to 240 V using **step-down transformers**.
- Transformers only step-up and step-down **alternating** voltages.

## Now try this

**c** Find the following key words in this wordsearch.

national     grid     voltage
current     cable     loss

| V | C | A | K | O | R | G | L |
|---|---|---|---|---|---|---|---|
| O | A | G | S | S | O | A | P |
| L | B | N | A | B | N | L | T |
| T | L | D | L | O | S | S | D |
| A | E | P | I | C | E | L | I |
| G | K | T | A | E | E | L | R |
| E | A | N | E | C | F | N | G |
| N | T | N | E | R | R | U | C |

## Homework

7 Draw a block diagram to show how energy from fossil fuels is transformed into electrical energy for use in our homes.

8 Make a list of electrical devices in the home that use step-down transformers.

9 Write a paragraph to explain why electricity is transmitted at high voltages.

# Generating electricity

## GENERATING ELECTRICITY

- A **dynamo** is a small electrical **generator**.
- In a dynamo or a generator, an electric **current** is **induced** in a **circuit** by moving a **coil** near a **magnet** or by moving a magnet near a coil.
- A generator produces an **alternating potential difference**.
- A generator in a power station consists of a coil of wire rotating between the poles of a magnet. The coil cuts the magnetic field lines and this induces a potential difference.

### Now try this

**a** Circle all the items needed to make a small electric generator.

battery     motor

resistor    coil

magnet      voltmeter

spring      wires

 **TOP TIP** A generator transforms kinetic energy into electrical energy.

### Homework

1  In your own words, describe how a generator produces electricity.
2  Use a diagram to show how an electric generator produces electricity.
3  Draw a labelled diagram of a bicycle dynamo.

## RENEWABLE AND NON-RENEWABLE FUELS

- **Non-renewable energy** resources will eventually run out.
- **Fossil fuels** like coal, natural gas and crude oil are non-renewable resources.
- **Nuclear fuels** like uranium and plutonium are non-renewable resources because they will eventually run out.
- **Renewable** resources of energy can be replaced as we use them or are resources that will be available for a very long time.
- **Biomass resources** like wood, straw and manure are renewable resources because they will not run out as long as chopped down trees are replaced.
- Examples of renewable energy resources: biomass, **hydroelectric**, **wind**, **tidal**, **wave**, **geothermal** and **solar**.

### Now try this

**b** Tick (✓) the correct column for each statement.

| Fuel | Renewable | Non-renewable |
|------|-----------|---------------|
| coal | ☐ | ☐ |
| uranium | ☐ | ☐ |
| straw | ☐ | ☐ |
| manure | ☐ | ☐ |
| crude oil | ☐ | ☐ |

### Homework

4  Make a table of renewable sources and non-renewable sources.
5  Explain why wood may be considered as a renewable fuel.
6  Use the Internet to find the percentage of electricity produced in the UK from renewable resources.

# POWER STATIONS

- The most common energy sources are coal, oil and gas. These are burned to produce heat.
- In **power stations**, the fuel is burned to heat water. This produces high-pressured steam to spin the **turbines**. The turbines turn the **generators** and this produces **electricity**. The **National Grid** is used to transmit electricity to consumers.
- Some power stations use uranium or plutonium as fuel. **Nuclear fission** reactions produce the heat in nuclear power stations.
- Energy from **renewable energy sources** is used to directly drive the turbines.
- A **wind turbine** changes the **kinetic energy** of the wind into **electrical energy**.
- Electricity can be produced directly from the Sun's radiation using **solar cells**.
- In some volcanic areas, hot water and steam rise to the surface. The steam can be tapped and used to drive turbines. This is **geothermal energy**.

## Now try this

**c** Fill in the missing words.

All power stations are designed to produce _____. In a nuclear power station, a fuel like _____ is used to heat the _____ to produce _____. The steam is used to turn the turbines, which in turn spin the generators.

## Homework

7 Draw a block diagram to show the stages in the production of electricity in a coal-burning power station.

8 Research and write about how a wind turbine produces energy.

9 Research and write about geothermal energy.

# THE ENVIRONMENT

- Fossil fuels are relatively cheap and produce large amounts of electricity. However, they give off harmful gases, like carbon dioxide, that cause **global warming**.
- **Wind turbines** do not produce any polluting waste and can be used in remote areas. However, wind turbines can be an eyesore. They also require lots of space and their electrical power depends on wind speed.
- **Solar cells** have a long life, do not produce polluting waste and require low maintenance. However, the initial cost of solar cells can be quite high.
- **Nuclear power stations** do not produce **greenhouse gases** like carbon dioxide and therefore do not contribute to global warming.
- Nuclear power stations produce **radioactive waste** that can be active for thousands of years.
- **Tidal power** and **wave power** can change the flow of water and destroy local habitats.

## Now try this

**d** Which of the following statements is/are correct?

**i** All fossil fuels release dangerous greenhouse gases. ☐

**ii** Fossil fuels are very expensive. ☐

**iii** Global warming may be due to burning fossil fuels. ☐

**iv** Solar cells work well at night. ☐

## Homework

10 Describe the advantages and disadvantages of using fossil fuels.

11 Describe the advantages and disadvantages of having hydroelectric power in the UK.

12 Explain why very few houses in the UK have solar cells to generate electricity.

# Electromagnetic waves

## UNDERSTANDING WAVES

- There are two types of **wave**: **longitudinal** and **transverse**.
- A longitudinal wave, like **sound**, has vibrations parallel to the direction of the wave velocity. A transverse wave has vibrations 90 degrees to the direction of the wave velocity.
- **Electromagnetic waves** are transverse waves.
- The **frequency** of a wave is the number of waves produced per unit of time.
- The **wavelength** of a wave is the distance between two neighbouring peaks.
- The speed ($v$) of the wave in metres per second (m/s) is related to its frequency ($f$) in hertz (Hz) and the wavelength ($\lambda$) in metres (m) by the equation: $v = f\lambda$.

### Now try this

**a** Circle the correct answer.

The speed of a wave is measured in:

m     m/s     Hz

Wavelength and amplitude can be measured in:

m     m/s     Hz

Frequency is measured in:

m     m/s     Hz

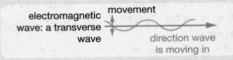

electromagnetic wave: a transverse wave / movement / direction wave is moving in

### Homework

1  Draw labelled diagrams to illustrate longitudinal and transverse waves.
2  Use the Internet to research and make a list of transverse waves other than electromagnetic waves.
3  Write a paragraph on the differences and similarities between longitudinal and transverse waves.

## ELECTROMAGNETIC WAVES

- **Electromagnetic waves** travel as waves and carry energy from one place to another.
- Electromagnetic waves have different **wavelengths** and **frequencies** but they travel at the same speed of 300 000 kilometres per second in a vacuum.
- The electromagnetic waves in the order of decreasing wavelength (or increasing frequency) are: **radio waves, microwaves, infrared** (IR), **visible light, ultraviolet** (UV), **X-rays** and **gamma rays**.

### Now try this

**b** Which of the following statements is/are true?

| Statement | True | False |
|---|---|---|
| i  All electromagnetic waves have the same frequency. | ☐ | ☐ |
| ii  Gamma rays have a longer wavelength than radio waves. | ☐ | ☐ |
| iii  In a vacuum, radio waves and microwaves have the same speed | ☐ | ☐ |
| iv  X-rays are transverse waves. | ☐ | ☐ |

**TOP TIP** All electromagnetic waves can be reflected.

visible spectrum

longest wavelength — shortest wavelength

| radio waves | micro-waves | infrared | ultra-violet | X-rays | gamma rays |

lowest frequency — highest frequency

### Homework

4  Summarise the main properties of electromagnetic waves.
5  Make a list of items in your home that emit electromagnetic waves. For each item, use the information given on page 257 to estimate the wavelength of the waves.
6  Use the Internet to find the distance of the Earth from the Sun. Use this to calculate the time it takes for light to travel from the Sun to Earth.

# USES AND HAZARDS OF ELECTROMAGNETIC WAVES

- Radio waves, microwaves, infrared waves and visible light can be used for **communication**.
- Humans do not absorb radio waves.
- Microwaves can heat human tissues.
- Infrared radiation can burn skin.
- Very intense visible light, for example lasers, can be harmful to the eyes.
- Ultraviolet radiation can cause **sunburn** and **cancer**.
- X-rays are used for **imaging** the human skeleton. X-rays pass through soft tissues but are absorbed by bones.
- Both X-rays and gamma rays can **mutate** cells and cause cancer.
- Higher frequency radiation (for example, gamma rays) is more harmful than low frequency radiation (for example, light).

## Now try this

**c** Circle the radiations that can cause cancer in humans.

radio waves

microwaves

infrared waves

visible light

ultraviolet waves

X-rays

gamma rays

## Homework

7  Draw a table to show the uses of electromagnetic waves.

8  Outline the hazards of electromagnetic waves.

9  Make a list of potentially hazardous items in the school laboratory that emit electromagnetic waves.

# COMMUNICATIONS

- **Radio waves** create an **alternating current** in an aerial of the same frequency as the radio wave.
- The **ionosphere** reflects radio waves. This helps long distance communication.
- Microwaves can pass through the Earth's atmosphere and are used for sending information between the Earth and **satellites**. They are used within mobile phone networks.
- **Infrared waves** and **visible light** can be used to send signals along **optical fibres** and so travel curved paths.
- Modern telecommunications systems use optical fibres to transmit data at high speed over very long distances.
- Communication signals may be **analogue** (continuously varying signals) or **digital** (only two values are possible).
- Digital signals are less prone to **interference** than analogue and are processed by computers.

## Now try this

**d** Circle the electromagnetic waves that can be used for communications.

radio waves

microwaves

infrared waves

visible light

ultraviolet waves

X-rays

gamma rays

## Homework

10  Draw a labelled diagram to show how optical fibres reflect light.

11  Explain what is meant by digital signals. Make a list of items in your home that use digital signals.

12  Draw a labelled diagram to show how radio waves can be used for both long-distance communications and for satellite communications.

# Radioactivity

## ALPHA, BETA AND GAMMA

- An **atom** has a small central **nucleus**, containing **protons** and **neutrons**, which is surrounded by **electrons**.
- Protons have a positive charge, neutrons have no charge and electrons have a negative charge.
- The protons and neutrons are also known as the **nucleons**.
- The nucleus of an atom may be represented as $^A_Z X$, where X is the **chemical symbol**, A is the nucleon or **mass number** and Z is the proton or **atomic number**.
- The **isotopes** of an element are nuclei that have the same number of protons but a different number of neutrons. For example: $^3_2 He$ and $^4_2 He$.
- **Radioactivity** is to do with unstable nuclei.
- The nucleus of a **radioactive** atom emits either an **alpha** ($\alpha$) particle or a **beta** ($\beta$) particle and/or **gamma** ($\gamma$) rays.

- All three radiations cause **ionisation**. This means that they can all strip off electrons when colliding with atoms.
- An alpha particle is a slow-moving **helium nucleus** (He). It is a good ioniser and has poor penetrating power. It can be stopped by a thin piece of paper.
- A beta particle is a fast-moving electron. It is a weak ioniser and can be stopped by a few millimetres of aluminium.
- Gamma rays are short-wavelength electromagnetic waves. They are very poor ionisers because they have no charge. They can be stopped by a few centimetres of lead.

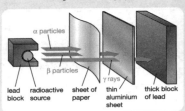

### Homework

1 Write a paragraph on radioactive nuclei.
2 Draw mind maps for alpha particles, beta particles and gamma rays.

## HALF-LIFE

- **Background radiation** is always present and is due to **radioactive** substances in rocks, soil and air, and **cosmic rays**.
- Some background radiation comes from man-made sources, from the nuclear industry and hospital waste.
- The **half-life** of a **radioactive isotope** is the average time taken for half the active nuclei to **decay** or disintegrate.
- After one half-life, the **activity** of the **source** or the **count rate** measured from the source will halve.
- The fraction of nuclei left after one half-life is half, after two half-lives is a quarter, after three half-lives is one-eighth and so on.

### Now try this

a Which of the following statements is/are correct?

i  All isotopes have the same half-life. ☐

ii A source containing isotopes of very short half-life will be very active. ☐

iii After one half-life, half of the nuclei have decayed. ☐

iv After two half-lives, a third of the active nuclei will be left. ☐

### Homework

3 Use the Internet to find some radioactive isotopes and their half-lives.
4 In your own words explain why a source will have a high activity if there are lots of nuclei and the half-life is very short.

# USE OF NUCLEAR RADIATIONS

- **Radioisotopes** are used as **tracers** in industry and hospitals.
- **Gamma** ray emitting tracers are used to find leaks or blockages in underground pipes.
- In medicine, the function of some vital organs can be diagnosed using a radioactive tracer.
- Gamma rays are used to sterilise bandages, syringes and other hospital instruments.
- Irradiating fresh fruit with gamma rays prolongs their shelf life.
- In **radiotherapy**, several gamma ray sources are directed towards cancerous tissues to destroy the cancer cells.
- Domestic smoke detectors contain an **alpha emitting source** (americium).
- The technique of **carbon dating** can be used to date bone, cloth, wood and paper.

 **TOP TIP** In a paper mill, a beta source can be used to monitor the thickness of the paper.

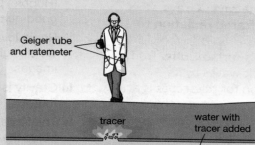

Geiger tube and ratemeter

tracer

water with tracer added

## Now try this

**b** Complete the sentences by filling in the missing words.

Leaks in pipes can be detected using a _____. A radioactive substance emitting gamma rays is put into the pipe. A gamma-emitting source is used because gamma rays can _____ through the pipe and soil. An _____ in the activity above the ground locates the leaks.

## Homework

5 Tracers are used in industry and in hospital. Make a list of all the applications.

6 Use the information in the student book (page 269) to explain in your own words how a smoke detector works.

7 Describe how a smoke detector works.

# SAFETY ISSUES

- All **ionising** radiations (alpha particles, beta particles and gamma rays) are dangerous.
- All ionising radiations can destroy healthy cells. They can also damage the DNA, leading to **mutation** of cells and cancer.

## Now try this

**c** Find the following key words in this wordsearch.

cancer
cells
alpha
beta
gamma
mutate

| R | K | B | N | E | E | T | U |
|---|---|---|---|---|---|---|---|
| R | A | E | T | I | N | M | O |
| E | V | T | P | O | U | L | G |
| C | A | A | G | T | S | R | F |
| N | L | T | A | L | P | H | A |
| A | G | T | E | E | N | Y | S |
| C | E | L | L | S | T | L | E |
| C | G | G | A | M | M | A | E |

## Homework

8 Describe how radiation workers protect themselves.

9 Make a list of the precautions you can take to minimise the dangers of using radioactive sources in the laboratory.

10 Make a list of places where you might be exposed to ionising radiation.

# The Universe

## OBSERVING SPACE AND GRAVITY

- Scientists use Earth-based **telescopes** and observations made from **space probes** (for example, Hubble) to observe the **planets**, **stars** and **galaxies**.
- **Optical telescopes** make use of light to form images. They can be made either from curved mirrors or lenses.
- **Radio telescopes** use radio waves to map out the sky.
- Astronomers also use **gamma rays**, **X-rays**, **ultraviolet radiation** and **infrared radiation** to make observations.
- Observations from the Earth's surface suffer from absorption of electromagnetic waves by its atmosphere. The best location for telescopes is at the top of mountains.
- The **Solar System** has been explored using both manned and unmanned spacecraft.
- All objects, for example planets, moons and stars, exert a **gravitational force**.
- **Gravity** is an attractive force.
- Gravitational force between planets and the Sun keeps planets in **orbit**.

### Now try this

**a** Which of the following statements are true? Place a tick (✓) in the correct column.

| Statement | True | False |
| --- | --- | --- |
| **i** Telescopes in space (Hubble) produce good quality images. | ☐ | ☐ |
| **ii** Radio telescopes use visible light to produce images. | ☐ | ☐ |
| **iii** Gravity is a repulsive force. | ☐ | ☐ |
| **iv** The force of gravity holds the Solar System together. | ☐ | ☐ |

 **TOP TIP** The gravitational force is larger for massive objects and it gets smaller for longer distances.

### Homework

1. Discuss the advantages and disadvantages of having telescopes such as Hubble in space.
2. Use a search engine to look at images produced by Hubble telescope. Make a list of some of these images for the class.
3. Make a list of objects that exert a large gravitational force.

## SOLAR SYSTEM

- Our **Sun** and the **Solar System** were formed from a huge mass of gas and dust particles.
- The planets in the order of increasing distance from the Sun are: Mercury, Venus, Earth, Mars, Jupiter, Saturn, Uranus, Neptune and Pluto.
- The rocky planets are: Mercury, Venus, Earth and Mars.
- The gas giants are: Jupiter, Uranus and Neptune.
- Our Moon was created by the collision of the Earth with another small planet during the formation of the Solar System.

### Now try this

**b** Arrange the following in the order of increasing distance from the Earth:

Pluto    Moon    Mars    Sun

### Homework

4. Make a mnemonic to remember the order of the planets from the Sun.
5. Use the Internet to obtain some interesting facts about your favourite planet.
6. Make a list of the differences between Mercury and Jupiter.

## LIFE AND DEATH OF STARS

- All **stars** are formed from interstellar dust and gas (hydrogen) clouds.
- **Gravitational forces** pull the gases and dust particles together, this is known as **gravitational collapse**. This increases the temperature.
- **Thermonuclear fusion** reactions between hydrogen nuclei start when the temperatures become too high.
- These nuclear reactions release energy in the form of heat and light. A star is born.
- A medium-mass star like our Sun will become a **red giant** and then a **planetary nebula** and a **white dwarf**.
- A heavy-mass star will become a red giant and then a **supernova** and either a **neutron star** or a **black hole**.
- A **black hole** is very dense and has a strong gravitational field from which even light cannot escape.

### Now try this

c A star is close to its death. Arrange the following stages in the correct sequence for a star like our Sun.

☐ red giant

☐ star

☐ planetary nebula

☐ white dwarf

### Homework

7  Use the information on page 285 of your student book to describe nuclear fusion.

8  Draw a mind map to show the end of a star like our Sun and one that is much more massive.

9  Research and write a few sentences about red giants, supernovas and black holes.

## THE EXPANDING UNIVERSE

- A **galaxy** is a cluster of stars.
- The **Universe** began from a sudden expansion of space some 15 billion years ago. This event is known as the **Big Bang**.
- The evidence that the Universe is expanding comes from the observation that all galaxies are moving away from each other.
- The early Universe was dense and very hot. Its **expansion** led to cooling. The temperature of the Universe is currently −270 °C.
- If a wave source (for example, a galaxy) is moving relative to an observer, then there will be a change in the observed **wavelength** or **frequency**. This is known as the **Doppler effect**.
- The spectrum of light from all galaxies moving away from us shows **red shift** (the entire spectrum is moved to longer wavelengths).
- The further away galaxies are, the greater their speed is and hence red shift is seen.
- If there is not enough matter in the Universe, it will expand forever.
- If there is enough matter in the Universe, gravity will slow down the expansion rate and eventually start to **contract** the Universe towards a **Big Crunch**.

### Now try this

d Circle the items that provide evidence of the Big Bang.

red shift

red giants

planets

space is at −270 °C

galaxies are moving away from us

black holes

### Homework

10  Discuss all the evidence that points to the creation of the universe.

11  Draw a labelled diagram to illustrate what is meant by red shift.

12  Describe how the fate of the Universe depends on the amount of matter.

# Evidence from marks and impressions

## FINGERPRINTS

- There are three quite different types of **fingerprint** pattern: loop, arch and whorl.
- Everyone, even identical twins, has different fingerprints.
- Fingerprints may be visible at a crime scene if they have left impressions in soft surfaces like soap or if the criminal had a coloured liquid, such as blood, on their hands.
- A third type of fingerprint is called '**latent**'. These are invisible but techniques are available to make them visible.
- Latent prints occur because oils present on the fingers due to perspiration leave invisible prints on surfaces.
- Latent prints on smooth dark surfaces are shown up by lightly brushing with grey aluminium powder.
- Latent prints on smooth light coloured surfaces are shown up by brushing with black carbon powder.

### Now try this

**a** Circle the correct answer.

Not a type of fingerprint

    whorl    arch    bridge

Used to lift prints from smooth white surfaces

    iodine    carbon    oils

Used to lift prints from smooth dark surfaces

    aluminium    carbon    iodine

Identical fingerprints are found on

    twins    sisters    no-one

### Homework

1  Describe **three** ways in which fingerprints may be left at a crime scene.
2  Explain what is meant by a latent fingerprint.
3  How would you reveal latent fingerprints left on white painted window frames?

## TYRE PRINTS

- If tyre tracks are found near a crime scene the area is closed to the public.
- It is important that crime scenes and samples are not **contaminated** so access is restricted and the forensic team wear protective clothing, such as overalls, masks, gloves and hairnets.
- A ruler is placed next to the track for scale and its photograph taken.
- A permanent plaster cast is then made of the track.
- This must be done quickly as changes of weather may cause loss in definition of the track.
- A cardboard support is placed around a good part of the track.
- Plaster of Paris is mixed with water then poured into the track and allowed to set. It is then examined back at the forensic laboratory.

### Now try this

**b** Number this list to show the order in which events must occur if a tyre track is found near a crime scene.

- [ ] Take a photograph of the track.
- [ ] Put a ruler by the track for scale.
- [ ] Place a cardboard support around the track.
- [ ] Pour the plaster into the support and allow it to set.
- [ ] Mix some plaster of Paris.
- [ ] Put a tape around the area to keep the public out.

### Homework

4  Construct a flowchart to show how a permanent record could be made of tyre tracks.
5  Look at a real car tyre and draw its various features.
6  Label your diagram to highlight the features that could be used to identify it.

# SHOE PRINTS

- Shoe prints may be left at the scene of a crime. These may be impressions left in soil or may be dust transferred onto smooth surfaces.
- Photographs including a scale are taken of the prints.
- Dry dust footprints can be lifted using an electrostatically charged plate which attracts the small dust particles when held just above it.
- Damp footprints can be dusted and lifted with sticky plastic sheets.
- Taking **casts** of impressions is better than photographing them because the quality of the print many be affected by shadows.
- Comparisons with databases of sole patterns can be made and this can often be used to identify the brand of shoe.
- The size of the shoe is found. Height and shoe size are proportional and therefore the height of the wearer can also be estimated.
- The sole of a shoe may have wear marks and distinctive marks which make it unique.

## Now try this

c **Which of the following characteristics may be determined from a shoe print?**

shoe brand

shoe size

race

sex

height

## Homework

7 On A4 paper, make a shoe print from your own shoes and label its distinctive features.

8 On the sheet write your shoe size and your height in metres.

9 Explain how you could show that shoe size and height are proportional to one another.

# TOOLS

- Tools may have been used to force entry and may leave characteristic marks on surfaces.
- If the tool can be found, any imperfection on its surface (such as a groove or nick on it) can be identified.
- A match can be made by using Plasticine to cast the impression of the groove on the tool and comparing this with marks at the scene.

## Homework

10 Search the Internet to find a picture that shows tool marks and print it out.

11 Explain how a cast could be made of these tool marks.

12 Why might tool marks be left at a crime scene?

# Identifying chemicals

## CHARACTERISTIC PROPERTIES OF CHEMICALS

- The **melting** and **boiling points** of substances can be used to identify them.
- How **soluble** a substance is in water is another property that can help to identify a substance.
- The **properties** of elements and compounds are determined by the type of structure and bonding present in them.
- Compounds may be covalent or ionic and these different types of bonding lead to very different properties.
- **Qualitative analysis** allows a forensic scientist to identify substances found at a crime scene.
- Simple test tube reactions can be carried out to identify many substances.

 **TOP TIP** Qualitative analysis involves finding out what a substance is but not how much of it there is.

### Now try this

**a** Complete these sentences by filling in the missing words.

_____ analysis is used to identify what a substance is. By finding a substance's _____ point or _____ point you might be able to find out what the substance is. Another useful test is to see if the substance is _____ in water. This depends on what type of _____ and _____ the compound has.

## Homework

1 Explain what determines the properties of a compound.
2 Look up the words 'qualitative' and 'quantitative' in a dictionary and say how they differ.
3 Give **three** properties of a substance that could be used to identify it.

## IONIC BONDING

- **Ionic bonding** occurs between a metal and a non-metal. The bonding in substances like sodium chloride and magnesium oxide is ionic.
- Metal atoms form positive ions and non-metal atoms form negative ions.
- These ions are held together by a strong electrostatic attraction and form a **giant lattice**.
- Since these strong attractions take a great deal of energy to overcome ionic substances have high melting and boiling points.
- If the attraction between ions is not too strong, then water may be able to pull the ions apart from each other and a substance will dissolve in water.
- If the attraction between the ions is very strong then water may not be able to separate the ions and the substance will be insoluble.

### Now try this

**b** Circle the correct answer.

The bonding between a metal and a non-metal is

covalent    convalent    ionic

The particles in sodium chloride are

ions    molecules    atoms

The charge on a magnesium ion is

2+    2–    0

The attraction between ions is

gravity    electrostatic    magnetic

 **TOP TIP** A lattice is a giant structure with a regular arrangement of particles, in this case, ions.

## Homework

4 What sort of bonding would you expect in the following compounds: **a)** NaF **b)** CO **c)** $H_2O$?
5 Explain why the boiling point of hydrogen chloride is low and that of magnesium chloride is high.
6 Why is calcium carbonate, an ionic compound, insoluble in water?

# WRITING THE FORMULA OF AN IONIC COMPOUND

- Follow this sequence to work out the formula for sodium bromide.
  - Look up the sodium ion on your data sheet ($Na^+$). Now look up the bromide ion ($Br^-$).
  - Choose the right amount of each ion so that there are the same number of + and −. In this case you need one of each ion so the formula is NaBr.
- Now try calcium iodide.
  - Calcium is $Ca^{2+}$; Iodine is $I^-$. For each $Ca^{2+}$ with a charge of 2+ you need two $I^-$ as each iodide has only a 1− charge. The formula is $CaI_2$.

## Now try this

**c** Circle the correct formula for each ionic compound.

calcium chloride
    CaCl    $Ca_2Cl$    $CaCl_2$

sodium oxide
    NaO    $Na_2O$    $NaO_2$

aluminium iodide
    $AlI_3$    AlI    $Al_3I$

## Homework

7 Write formulae for: **a)** sodium chloride **b)** magnesium oxide **c)** calcium sulfide **d)** lithium bromide.

8 Write formulae for: **a)** magnesium chloride **b)** calcium iodide **c)** barium fluoride **d)** lithium oxide.

9 Write formulae for: **a)** aluminium sulfide **b)** iron (II) oxide **c)** iron (III) oxide.

# ORGANIC COMPOUNDS

- Many substances from living materials are **organic**, they are **compounds** of carbon.
- Organic compounds are bonded together by **covalent bonds** which involves the outer electrons of the atoms in the compound being shared. The bonding that holds the atoms together is very strong.
- The groups of atoms which are bonded together form molecules. Molecules attract each other but the attraction is not very strong.
- The forces of attraction between molecules can easily be overcome so these compounds have low melting and boiling points.
- You should know the names and formulae of these molecules: carbon dioxide ($CO_2$), water ($H_2O$), ethanol ($C_2H_5OH$), glucose ($C_6H_{12}O_6$).
- To test for an alcohol, such as ethanol, you warm a little of the sample with acidified potassium dichromate, which changes from orange to green.
- To test for glucose, heat it with Benedict's solution. The blue solution forms a brick red precipitate.

## Now try this

**d** Circle the correct answer.

Formula for glucose
    $C_2H_5OH$    $C_6H_{12}O_6$    $C_6H_{10}O_6$

Name of $C_2H_5OH$
    glucose    propanol    ethanol

Covalent bonds are
    weak    long    strong

Acidified potassium dichromate is
    green    blue    orange

When glucose is present, Benedict's solution turns
    blue    green    brick red

 Covalent bonds ARE STRONG but molecules are held together by WEAK INTERMOLECULAR forces.

## Homework

10 Make a poster which teaches about covalent bonding.

11 Draw a series of diagrams to show how you would test for alcohol.

12 Use the Internet to find out about how some breathalysers test for alcohol and write down **five** different facts that you have learnt.

# Qualitative analysis of ionic compounds

## FLAME TESTS

- **Flame tests** are used to test for some metals. The following flame colours are observed:

| | |
|---|---|
| Lithium Li$^+$ – bright red | Barium Ba$^{2+}$ – green |
| Potassium K$^+$ – lilac | Calcium Ca$^{2+}$ – brick red |
| Sodium Na$^+$ – orange/yellow | |

- To carry out a flame test, a **nichrome wire** is first cleaned by placing it in a small amount of concentrated hydrochloric acid and then placing it in a blue Bunsen flame.
- The wire is then dipped into some fresh concentrated hydrochloric acid and then into a small amount of the solid.
- The wire is then held in the Bunsen flame and the colour noted.

### Now try this

**a** Circle the correct answer. There may be more than one correct answer.

  **i** A green flame shows

      Li$^+$    Ba$^{2+}$    calcium ions

  **ii** An orange/yellow flame shows

      Ca$^{2+}$    Na$^+$    sodium ions

  **iii** A lilac flame shows

      K$^+$    Ca$^{2+}$    potassium ions

  **iv** A red flame shows

      Ca$^{2+}$    Li$^+$    calcium ions

### Homework

1. Use an image search on the Internet to find pictures of flame tests. Print them out.
2. If you do not have a colour printer then colour the flames in your printout.
3. Try to find at least **three** different coloured flames and label each picture to say what metal it is.

## PRECIPITATION REACTIONS

- The presence of some metal ions can be shown by adding some sodium hydroxide solution and looking to see if a **precipitate** (ppt) appears.

| | |
|---|---|
| Copper(II) Cu$^{2+}$ | forms a blue ppt of copper(II) hydroxide |
| Iron(II) Fe$^{2+}$ | forms a dull green ppt of iron(II) hydroxide |
| Iron(III) Fe$^{3+}$ | forms a rusty ppt of iron(III) hydroxide |
| Lead(II) Pb$^{2+}$ | forms a white ppt of lead(II) hydroxide which redissolves in an excess of NaOH |
| Calcium Ca$^{2+}$ | forms a slight white ppt of calcium hydroxide |

- We can test for the chloride ions, Cl$^-$, by adding dilute nitric acid followed by silver nitrate solution. If Cl$^-$ ions are present, a white precipitate will form.
- Sulfate ions (SO$_4^{2-}$) can be identified by adding hydrochloric acid followed by barium chloride solution. A white precipitate forms.

### Now try this

**b** Circle the correct answer. Which ion is present if we get:

a white ppt with HCl$_{(aq)}$ and barium chloride

    Cl$^-$    SO$_4^{2-}$    CO$_3^{2-}$

a slight white ppt with NaOH$_{(aq)}$

    Cl$^-$    Na$^+$    Ca$^{2+}$

a white ppt with NaOH$_{(aq)}$ that redissolves in excess

    Ca$^{2+}$    Pb$^{2+}$    Fe$^{2+}$

a brown ppt with NaOH$_{(aq)}$

    Fe$^{2+}$    Na$^+$    Fe$^{3+}$

### Homework

4. Draw, label and colour a diagram to show all the precipitates in the table above.
5. Draw and label 'before' and 'after' diagrams to show how you would test for a chloride.
6. Draw and label 'before' and 'after' diagrams to show how you would test for a sulfate.

## TESTING FOR CARBONATE IONS

- Carbonate ions have the formula $CO_3^{2-}$.
- Adding dilute hydrochloric acid to any carbonate releases carbon dioxide gas.
- We can test for carbon dioxide by bubbling the gas through **limewater**.
- If carbon dioxide is present, the limewater turns milky.

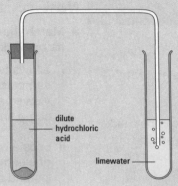

dilute hydrochloric acid

limewater

### Now try this

**c** Complete these sentences by filling in the gaps.

A geologist thinks she has a piece of limestone, containing calcium carbonate, and asks you to test it. You decide to add some _____ _____ and notice that a gas is made. To check that the gas is _____ _____ you pass the gas through _____ and it turns _____ because the rock was limestone.

### Homework

7  Draw a diagram to show how you would test for carbon dioxide gas.

8  Find out the names of as many rocks as you can that contain calcium carbonate.

9  What would a geologist do to test for a carbonate?

## PREDICTING WHAT PRECIPITATE FORMS

- Precipitates are formed because the substance is not **soluble** in water.
- We can work out what precipitate forms if we know which substances are soluble or **insoluble**.

|  | Soluble | Insoluble |
|---|---|---|
| bases | ammonia, group 1 hydroxides, calcium hydroxide (slightly) | all other oxides and hydroxides of metals |
| carbonates | group 1 | all other carbonates |
| sulfates | most | except lead, barium and calcium sulfate (slightly) |
| nitrates | all |  |
| chlorides | most | except silver and lead chloride |

- If a precipitate forms when lead nitrate and potassium sulfate are added together we know the precipitate must be lead sulfate, which is insoluble, because potassium nitrate is soluble.

### Now try this

**d** Use the table on the left to work out the products formed when the following solutions are mixed. Write (ppt) after the one that forms a precipitate.

sodium sulfate + lead nitrate

_____  _____

silver nitrate + sodium chloride

_____  _____

potassium sulfate + barium hydroxide

_____  _____

iron(II) chloride + sodium hydroxide

_____  _____

copper(II) sulfate + potassium hydroxide

_____  _____

### Homework

10  Look up 'precipitate' in a dictionary and explain what a chemical precipitate is.

11  Draw a labelled diagram to show what happens when NaOH and $CaCl_2$ are mixed.

12  Draw a coloured and labelled diagram to show what happens when $CuCl_2$ and NaOH are mixed.

# Tools for the job

## INSTRUMENTS USED IN A FORENSIC LABORATORY

- More expensive equipment is available in the forensic laboratory than you have at school.
- This equipment is more powerful, can give more accurate results and uses very small samples of material.
- A **comparison microscope** allows you to look at two samples at the same time so easy comparisons can be made.
- A **polarising microscope** is like an ordinary microscope but uses polarised light instead of ordinary light. It is used on fibres, glass, ceramics and even metals.
- Polarising microscopes are good for identifying stress patterns in materials.
- **Electron microscopes** are good for looking at extremely small objects as they give much bigger magnification than ordinary light microscopes (more than 1000 times more).

### Now try this

**a** Match the type of microscope to its operation.

| | |
|---|---|
| **i** allows two samples to be viewed at the same time | polarising microscope |
| **ii** uses a beam of electrons instead of light | comparison microscope |
| **iii** uses polarised light to light up the sample | electron microscope |

### Homework

1. What are the advantages of analytical instruments used in a forensic laboratory?
2. List the **three** different types of microscope and say what each is used for.
3. On the Internet do an image search for an interesting electron micrograph and print it out.

## FIBRES

- **Fibres** can be lifted using sticky tape or tweezers, placed into a suitable container and labelled.
- A simple light microscope will be able to show: colour and pattern, whether natural or synthetic, thickness, texture (for example, smooth or crimped), cross-sectional area.
- A comparison microscope would be more useful if the fibre was being compared with another to get a match.
- An electron microscope would be better if more detail was needed.
- A match between a fibre found on a suspect and one from a crime scene does not necessarily mean the suspect has committed a crime.

 Make sure you don't say that a feature of a fibre that could usefully be recorded is its length!

### Now try this

**b** Which of the following useful features of a fibre could be observed using a light microscope?

size

colour

texture

pattern

length

type

### Homework

4. What features would a light microscope show on fibres?
5. On the Internet do an image search for an electron micrograph of a wool fibre and print it out.
6. What details can you see on the picture?

# PAINT

- A simple light microscope will be able to show: colour, number of layers, thickness, sequence of layers.
- A comparison microscope would be better if a paint chip was being compared with another to get a match.
- An electron microscope would be better if more detail was needed.
- A match between a chip of paint found at a vehicle accident scene and that found missing from a suspect's car would give quite strong evidence.

## Now try this

c Put these sentences in the right order to explain how evidence from a hit and run accident leads to a conviction.

- ☐ Place in evidence bag and label accurately.
- ☐ Return sample to laboratory for examination.
- ☐ Collect sample of paint found at crime scene.
- ☐ Attend court and deliver evidence.
- ☐ Use comparison microscope to match the two samples.
- ☐ Prepare a report.
- ☐ Visit suspect's home and remove sample of paint from freshly damaged car.

## Homework

7  What features would a light microscope be able to reveal about paint layers?

8  Do an image search on the Internet for an image of paint layers and print it out.

9  What details can you see on the picture?

# BULLETS AND SOIL

- The following features of a bullet can be observed using a light or comparison microscope: size (calibre), kind, residues on bullet, shape, marks or scratches on bullet, metal it is made of.
- Soil is collected with a vacuum, brush and container or tweezers as appropriate.
- The following features of a soil can be investigated by a forensic scientist: size of particles, shape of particles, organic content, water content, colour, pH of water derived from the soil.

## Now try this

d Fill in the missing words in these sentences.

When a bullet is fired it may become marked or _____ as it leaves the gun. These marks can be compared if a suspect's gun is found. The suspect's gun would be used to fire a bullet of the _____ type and it would be observed under a _____ microscope to see if there was a match.

## Homework

10  What types of microscope are used for looking at bullets?

11  Draw a diagram of a bullet and label the features that might be seen on it.

12  Describe how a soil sample may be used to help solve a crime.

# Blood typing

- **Blood** samples are obtained using a cotton wool swab or by cutting out the piece of material with blood on. The blood is then removed from the swab or material by soaking it in water.
- **Blood typing** can tell us if blood is human or animal and a person's blood group.
- **DNA** can be extracted from blood, semen or saliva.
- Enzymes can be used to cut DNA up into fragments which can then be separated using electrophoresis to give a **DNA profile**.
- DNA profiles of samples from a crime scene can be matched against those of suspects to include or exclude them from enquiries.
- DNA profiles can be used to show whether people are related or not.

## Now try this

**a** Complete these sentences by filling in the missing words.

DNA profiles are very useful to the forensic scientist. They are obtained by a process called _____ which uses fragments of DNA formed by treating the sample with _____ and then carrying out a process called _____. The DNA itself can be obtained from samples of _____, _____ and _____. Not only can the information be used to see if a suspect might have been at a crime scene but it can also tell us if people are _____.

## Homework

1  What different types of biological evidence are used by the police?
2  What is a DNA profile?
3  What information can be found out from a blood sample?

## BLOOD

- Blood has four components: plasma, blood platelets, white blood cells and red blood cells.
- Red blood cells can be seen if the blood is looked at through a microscope.
- White blood cells can only be seen under a microscope if they are stained first.
- Plasma is 90 per cent water but contains dissolved salts and carries antibodies to fight disease.
- Platelets are needed to form blood clots. Without platelets your blood would not clot if you were cut and you would bleed to death.
- The four main **blood groups** are: A, B, AB and O.
- Many people may have the same blood group but AB is more rare than the others. Blood group O is very common.

## Now try this

**b** Circle the correct answer.

not a component of blood
   platelets     plasma     veins

not a blood group
   AB     O     C

needed to make blood clot
   plasma     platelets     platters

common blood group
   AB     B     O

## Homework

4  What are the **four** basic components of blood?
5  Find an image of some red blood cells and carefully draw at least **three** of them.
6  Try to find out which blood group at least **one** member of your family has.

# DNA

- **DNA** is found in the nucleus of our cells. Every individual has unique DNA. No two people, except identical twins, have exactly the same DNA.
- Children inherit their DNA from their parents which means that there will be similarities in the DNA of people who are related to each other.
- **Electrophoresis** can be used on small samples of material obtained from saliva, blood or semen. DNA for electrophoresis testing is first chopped up into fragments using enzymes.
- Electrophoresis separates the fragments of DNA because the different fragments have different sizes and charges.
- Positively charged fragments move towards the negative electrode and negatively charged fragments move towards the positive electrode.
- Smaller, more highly charged particles move faster than large fragments with small charges. This allows the different fragments to be separated.

## Now try this

c Put these sentences in order to explain how the DNA profiles of two people are compared.

A positive DNA fragments travel to the negative electrodes

B carry out electrophoresis

C and negative fragments travel to the positive electrodes

D the DNA profiles of the two people are matched

E the fragments separate out forming a pattern of bands

F chop the DNA into fragments using enzymes

## Homework

7 Explain why DNA is such a useful source of biological material for the police.

8 Make a flowchart to show how electrophoresis works.

9 Go to http://gslc.genetics.utah.edu/units/biotech/gel/ and try your own DNA separation.

# DRAWING CONCLUSIONS FROM DNA AND BLOOD GROUP INFORMATION

- If blood at a crime scene matches that of a suspect, it is not evidence that the suspect was present at the crime, as many people share the same blood group. It tells you the suspect might have been at the crime scene.
- The type of blood group matched gives more information if the blood group is rare.
- DNA evidence is much more useful. Matching the DNA profile of blood obtained from a crime scene tells you the person must have been at the scene.
- It does not tell you when they were there or if they committed a crime, however.

 **TOP TIP** The more evidence the forensic team can collect, the more certain is their case.

## Now try this

d Place these pieces of evidence in order to say how strong the evidence is to prove a suspect committed a murder.

A match has been found between the suspect's blood or DNA and:

A group AB blood found at the scene.

B the DNA profile from blood found on the murder weapon.

C group A blood found at the scene.

D the DNA profile from blood found at the scene.

E group O blood was found at the scene.

## Homework

10 Which blood group gives the least promising clues and why?

11 Which blood group gives the most promising clues and why?

12 If we find a match between your DNA and that at the scene of a crime, what does this tell us?

# Plastic and glass

## COLLECTION OF FRAGMENTS

- At a crime scene, the position of **fragments** of glass should be recorded using a sketch or photograph. The fragments must then be collected carefully and placed in labelled containers.
- Fragments found at the scene can be matched with those found attached to a suspect's clothing.
- The match can be made by measuring the **refractive index** of the glass or plastic. The refractive index is a measure of how the material bends or refracts light.

 **TOP TIP** Light always bends towards the normal when it enters a glass or plastic block.

### Now try this

**a** Complete these sentences by filling in the missing words.

When light passes through plastic or _____ it is bent or _____.

The _____ index of glass found at a crime scene can be measured and compared with the refractive _____ of small splinters of glass found attached to a suspect's jacket.

### Homework

1 What is the refractive index a measure of?

2 What type of materials do we measure the refractive index of?

3 How does light bend when it enters a block of glass?

## WHAT IS THE REFRACTIVE INDEX?

- Light that is passing into a glass block is called the **incident ray**.
- When light passes into a glass (or plastic) block, it is bent or **refracted** towards the normal.
- The normal is a line drawn at right angles to the block at the point at which the light enters.
- The angle between the incident ray and the normal is called the **angle of incidence** and is shown by an '*i*'.
- The ray that passes through the block is called the **refracted ray**. The angle between the refracted ray and the normal is called the **angle of refraction** and is shown by an '*r*'.
- The **refractive index** is calculated by finding the value of $\dfrac{\sin i}{\sin r}$
- For any sample of the same glass, the angles and the refractive index will be the same.

### Now try this

**b** Add these labels to the diagram: angle of incidence, angle of refraction, incident ray, normal, refracted ray.

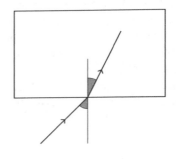

### Homework

4 Draw a diagram to show: incident and refracted rays, normal, angle of incidence and refraction.

5 Which of these must we measure to find the refractive index of a material?

6 Perspex has a refractive index of 1.495. Find out the refractive index of polystyrene.

# MEASURING THE REFRACTIVE INDEX OF FRAGMENTS OF GLASS

- Because glass fragments are not a regular shape like the glass block, their refractive index cannot be measured in the same way.
- Instead, a fragment of glass is placed in some oil and the oil is heated.
- Heating the oil changes its refractive index.
- The refractive index of the oil at different temperatures has already been measured.
- The point at which the oil's refractive index becomes the same as that of the glass, the fragment disappears from view.
- The refractive index of the oil at this temperature is looked up and this tells us the refractive index of the glass.

## Now try this

**c** Put these sentences in order to explain how the refractive index of a fragment of glass can be measured.

**A** The test is repeated several times and an average temperature found.

**B** The refractive index of the oil at that temperature is looked up.

**C** Heating is continued slowly until the fragment just disappears.

**D** The oil is heated.

**E** A piece of the glass is placed in oil in a glass container.

## Homework

7 Why do we need a special method to measure the refractive index of glass fragments?

8 Draw a series of labelled diagrams to show how the refractive index of a glass shard is found.

9 Why do you think the refractive index of oil changes when it is heated?

# Databases

## HOW ARE KEPT RECORDS USED?

- **Dental records** and **medical records** can be accessed to help identification.
- The **DVLC database** holds records of cars and their owners and can be useful if a car registration has been recorded.
- The DVLC database has details on the colour, make and model of a car. It will also tell you the engine capacity, date of registration, current owner and previous owners.
- Insurance companies keep records of valuable items.
- A national **DNA database** contains records obtained from people who have been taken into custody by the police.
- Police records exist of **fingerprints** of convicted criminals.
- Police records also contain photographs, sketches and descriptions of people.

### Now try this

**a** Place these events in the correct order.

**A** Dental records of the corpse and those held at the dental surgery are checked to confirm the identity of the dead person.

**B** The number is matched against the DVLC database.

**C** Police visit the address of the car owner. Nobody is in.

**D** A body is found in a car. There are no identification papers on it.

**E** The car registration is taken.

**F** Police note that an appointment card from a dentist is pinned to a notice board.

## Homework

1  Name the different types of records that hold information about us.
2  When do police keep a record of your DNA?
3  What other information might be held in police records that could be used in identification?

## MEDICAL INFORMATION

- Dental records give information on number of teeth, fillings, dentures, and any work that has been carried out to put crowns, bridges or braces on a person.
- The information from these records can be used to match them against the teeth of a victim.
- Dental records are particularly useful as most people visit a dentist whereas fewer have records obtained because of criminal behaviour.
- A match with dental records would give evidence of the address, gender, age and telephone number of a person.
- Medical records can give information on diseases a person has suffered from and any operations carried out on them. X-rays can give information about previously broken bones.
- A sample of DNA can be obtained from mouth scrapes or from hair roots of suspects and matched against evidence found at a crime scene.

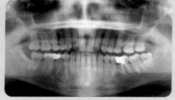

- A **DNA profile** can be matched against national databases.

### Now try this

**b** Circle the part of the statement in bold that is correct.

Some blood has been found at a murder scene and is blood-typed. The blood type is AB and that of the victim is O which tells us that the blood **does/does not** belong to the victim. A suspect has blood type AB. This **tells us/does not tell us** that the suspect killed the victim. Some DNA is extracted from the blood and a sample of **hair root/fingerprint** is taken from the suspect to compare the DNA. There is a match. This **tells us/does not tell us** that the suspect is the murderer. Further evidence is sought.

## Homework

4  What information could be obtained from your dental records?
5  How could a sample of DNA be obtained from you?
6  What information can medical records give about people?

# WITNESS DESCRIPTIONS

- The most important information from witness identification is description of **facial features** as these are unique to that person.
- Witnesses sometimes find it difficult to give accurate descriptions and different techniques have been developed to help them.
- One such technique is to use a **photo-fit** or **identikit** in order to build up a **composite** of the face being described.
- Information built up from witness descriptions can be used to produce 'Wanted' posters on which a suspect's image is displayed. They can also be used on television appeals.
- Features that are recorded are: height, build, scars, tattoos, clothes, age, birthmarks and sex.

### Now try this

c **Complete the sentences by filling in the missing words.**

A witness is trying to give a description of a possible suspect. An artist is helping her to build a _____ of the person's face. As well as the person's face, the witness is asked to describe the person's _____, the colour and length of their _____ and what _____ they were wearing. Meanwhile, the suspect has rushed back home to cut their _____ and burn their _____.

 Witness descriptions may be unreliable as it is possible to change the colour of hair, eyes and facial hair.

## Homework

7  Go to http://www.casebook.org/witnesses/ and read the witness descriptions of Jack the Ripper
8  Print it out and highlight the bits of information that are the most useful in identifying the Ripper.
9  Find a 'Wanted' poster for Jack the Ripper. If you can't, draw what you think he looked like.

# How to think like a dietician

## HOW DIETICIANS THINK

- **Dieticians** enquire into people's diets and make recommendations about how they can be improved in order to maintain or improve their health.
- Dieticians identify potentially health-damaging deficiencies in an individual's diet by drawing on their knowledge of which foods provide which **nutrients**.
- Dieticians draw on established dietary guidelines to say that people are healthier if their diets are low in fats and sugar, high in vitamins and high in fibre.
- Dieticians recommend foods (and hence nutrients) that may help people with particular needs, for example, women during pregnancy.

### Now try this

**a** What kind of diet is generally considered to be 'healthy'?

_____

**b** What is the 'five a day' campaign?

_____

**c** Check out the tips at:
http://www.eatwell.gov.uk/healthydiet/8tips/

 **TOP TIP** Watch the news for food stories, then demonstrate your knowledge in the exam where appropriate.

### Homework

1. How much fat is in a 'Big Mac'? Write down **six** fast food facts using a nutrition table like the one at: http://www.mcdonalds.com/app_controller.nutrition.categories.nutrition.index.html/
2. Write a newspaper article about the claim that honey is a healthier sweetener than sugar.
3. A woman is planning to get pregnant. What should she eat and why? Use this website to help you: http://www.eatwell.gov.uk/agesandstages/pregnancy/

## WHAT ARE NUTRIENTS?

- **Nutrients** come from food.
- We need them for energy and for our bodies to work properly.
- There are seven types of nutrient:
  - carbohydrates (sugar, starch and fibre)
  - proteins
  - lipids (fats and oils)
  - vitamins
  - minerals
  - water
- **Essential nutrients** are substances that cannot be manufactured in the body and must be obtained from foods that contain them.

 **TOP TIP** Definition: 'Nutrients are substances in food that the body can use to obtain energy, synthesise tissues, or regulate functions.'

### Homework

4. What are minerals?
5. Why do you need iron, calcium, phosphorus and zinc? Use this website to help you: http://www.eatwell.gov.uk/healthydiet/nutritionessentials/vitaminsandminerals/
6. Which minerals are essential?

# WHY DO WE NEED NUTRIENTS?

- We need a variety of nutrients to carry out the processes of life.
- Carbohydrates, fats and proteins provide energy.
- Proteins also build body tissue.
- Fats are used in the cell membrane, for insulation, to protect organs and to carry **fat-soluble vitamins**.
- Vitamins and minerals are needed in small amounts for the body to work properly.
- Water is an essential nutrient: our blood is mostly water and the chemical reactions in our cells use water.

 **TOP TIP** We need about eight glasses of water a day.

### Now try this

**d** Which **four** vitamins are fat soluble?

_____

**e** Which organs have a layer of fat and why?

_____

**f** Which body tissues are largely made of proteins?

_____

## Homework

7 Prepare a PowerPoint presentation on the effects of dehydration.

8 Are you drinking enough water and why does it matter? Use this website to help you: http://www.eatwell.gov.uk/healthydiet/nutritionessentials/drinks/drinkingenough/

9 Write an 'Agony Aunt' letter to a student who is skipping breakfast in order to lose weight.

# VITAMIN FACTS

- **Vitamins** are small molecules that we need to keep us healthy.
- For example, we need vitamin A to produce retinal, which in turn enables our eyes to sense light. Without it we would go blind.
- Most vitamins are essential, which means we can only get them from food.
- **Water-soluble vitamins** may be lost when food is cooked in water. To prevent this, serve food raw or avoid immersing food in cooking water or including water in the finished dish.
- Water-soluble vitamins are carried around the body in the bloodstream and any excess is eliminated in urine. These vitamins need to be consumed regularly.
- **Fat-soluble vitamins** are stored in your fat cells and liver and can be consumed less frequently.

 **TOP TIP** The usual source of vitamin B12 is meat. Vegetarians may choose to take a B12 supplement.

### Now try this

**g** Research vitamin A and answer the following questions.

**i** Is the vitamin soluble in fat or water?

_____

**ii** How is the vitamin used in the body?

_____

_____

**iii** What are the symptoms of being deficient in this vitamin?

_____

_____

**iv** Give examples of foods which contain this vitamin.

_____

_____

## Homework

10 Pretend you are a sailor in the eighteenth century who is suffering from scurvy and write a series of 'diary entries'.

11 What is scurvy? Which foods helped sailors to overcome it?

12 Research the following vitamins: B, C, D and K and answer questions **i** to **iv** in 'Now try this' question **g** above.

# You are what you eat (and drink)

## HEALTHY EATING

- Most foods contain a mixture of **nutrients** but some are especially high in one or another.
- The **food pyramid** on the right indicates the proportions of the different types of food that you need to eat in order to get the right balance of nutrients.
- Breads and cereals are rich in carbohydrates and should form the main part of your diet.
- Chocolates and cakes are high in sugar and fat and should be eaten sparingly.

**TOP TIP** Cut out or print out a food pyramid and stick it on your wall.

### Now Try This

**a** How much energy do we need? Complete the statements using these numbers: 3500, 2500, 2100, 1900, 40–60

A female teenager needs about _____ kilocalories a day.

A male teenager needs about _____ kilocalories a day.

A typical woman needs about _____ kilocalories a day.

An adult male athlete needs about _____ kilocalories a day.

The percentage of your daily energy needs that should ideally come from complex carbohydrates is _____.

### Homework

1. Visit http://www.eatwell.gov.uk/agesandstages/teens/ and summarise an article of your choice.
2. Give **three** examples to illustrate the size of a portion of fruit and vegetables. Repeat for a portion of milk products.

## PROTEINS

- Meat, fish, eggs and beans are good sources of **protein**.
- During digestion, proteins are broken down into **amino acids**.
- Amino acids are used for bones, growth and repair, to make antibodies, hormones and more.
- Protein can be used for energy if the supply of fat and carbohydrate is inadequate.
- About nine amino acids are '**essential**' which means that they must be supplied by the diet.
- Non-essential amino acids can be built inside the body from nitrogen, carbon, hydrogen and oxygen.
- A '**complete protein**' (as found in meat and eggs) is a protein which contains all of the essential amino acids.
- There are no complete proteins in plants, so vegetarians must eat a combination of plants to get all of the essential amino acids.

### Now try this

**b** Insert these words correctly into the following sentence:

proteins   digestion
build   hair

_____ are broken down into amino acids during _____ and used to _____ and repair muscles, skin and _____ cells.

### Homework

3. Summarise **three** types of vegetarian diet including vegan and lacto vegetarianism.
4. How would you test a food to find out how much protein it contains?

# CARBOHYDRATES: SUGAR

- There are two main types of **carbohydrates**: sugars and starches.
- **Sugars** are simple carbohydrates. They are small molecules that are quickly digested.
- **Glucose** is the so called 'blood sugar'. Cells absorb glucose from the blood and convert it into energy.
- **Fructose** (fruit sugar) and sucrose (table sugar) are converted into glucose.
- After eating sugary foods, glucose enters the bloodstream quickly, giving a 'blood sugar hit', which feels great.
- Blood sugar levels then fall. The hormone insulin helps glucose enter the cells. It also transports any excess to the liver and muscles where it is stored as **glycogen**.
- People with **diabetes** produce insufficient insulin to regulate blood sugar.

## Now try this

**c** Fill in the missing words.

glycogen    glycogen    water

Converting _____ into energy takes water. Dieters lose weight fast at first because they are losing _____ to convert glycogen. The body's fat stores are only opened once _____ stores are empty.

**TOP TIP** Table sugar has no fibre, vitamins or minerals and is considered to be an unhealthy energy source.

## Homework

5   Write a (fictitious, but scientifically accurate) radio interview with someone who has diabetes.

6   What is hypoglycaemia?

7   Design a leaflet for a sports club explaining how sports and energy drinks work.

# STARCHES AND FIBRES

- Cereals/grains (bread, rice, pasta, oats and so on) and potatoes and parsnips provide **complex carbohydrates**.
- Complex carbohydrates consist of chains of 300–1000 glucose molecules. Plants store energy by chaining glucose molecules up to make **starch** and **fibre**.
- Starch is broken down into glucose during digestion. This means the glucose enters the blood gradually (no sudden sugar hit).
- Some starchy foods, such as rice and potatoes, are now known to break down quickly and raise blood sugar levels quickly.
- Once the glucose is in the blood, it is taken in by cells and the excess is stored as glycogen.
- Fibre cannot be broken down and passes through the body undigested.

**TOP TIP** The Glycaemic Index (or GI) is a ranking of foods from 0 to 100 that tells us how fast and how far blood sugar rises after you eat a food that contains carbohydrates.

## Now try this

**d** Which of the following statements about carbohydrates are true?

Carbohydrates:

**i**   come from food.  ☐

**ii**   have a sugar molecule as their basic building block.  ☐

**iii**   should supply over half your daily energy needs.  ☐

**iv**   include simple carbohydrates (sugars) and complex carbohydrates (starches).  ☐

**v**   are converted into minerals in the body.  ☐

## Homework

8   List **five** starchy foods and make a note of the Glycaemic Index of each one.

9   Explain how to test a food to see if it has a high starch content.

10   Visit an online virtual laboratory and try the experiment in question **9**. Search for 'starch iodine virtual lab'.

# Fats, cholesterol and salt

## GETTING FAT ON FATS

- Dietary **fats** are broken down during digestion into smaller units. They then pass into the bloodstream.
- 95% of dietary fat is stored. In comparison, dietary carbohydrates supply immediate energy needs.
- Fat is stored in fatty tissues in the abdomen, under the skin, in blood vessels and in organs.
- Stored fats are only accessed to supply energy once glucose and glycogen stores run out.
- Note that overeating of any kind can lead to weight gain. If energy intake is greater than energy use, the excess is converted into body fat.

### Now try this

**a** Complete the sentences by filling in the missing words.

At 9 kilocalories per gram, _____ provide more energy per gram than other types of food. _____ and proteins provide 4 kilocalories per gram. _____ is the body's chosen way to store _____ because each gram holds a lot of kilocalories.

### Homework

1 How would you test a food to find out how much fat it contains?
2 Fats are not all bad. Explain why we need dietary fats.
3 One slice of pizza has 13 g of fat. List **five** more fatty foods.

## CHOLESTEROL

- **Cholesterol** is a waxy substance which the body uses to build cell membranes. It is in some foods and is also made by the liver.
- Cholesterol is carried round the body in the blood. Excess cholesterol is deposited in organs and arteries, and forms an unhealthy plaque.
- This reduces blood flow, damages organs and causes heart disease.
- Dieticians used to think that people could lower their cholesterol levels just by switching to a **low cholesterol diet**. We now know that cholesterol is largely made by the liver (and does not come from food).
- However, you can lower your cholesterol level by changing your diet and, in particular, the type of fats you eat.

### Now try this

**b** Circle the correct answer.

In the UK the main cause of death is:
heart disease     road deaths     AIDS

It is widely reported that heart disease kills one British adult every:
month     day     3 minutes

Heart disease can be caused by plaque building up in the:
coronary artery     biceps and triceps     legs

To lower our risk of heart disease, we should eat:
more salt     less saturated fat     more vitamin C

Blocked arteries mean that the heart is starved of oxygen, this is called:
angina     tuberculosis     aspartame

### Homework

4 List **20** bullet points about heart disease. (Try http://www.bbc.co.uk/health/conditions/heart/ for information.)
5 Apart from diet, what other factors affect the risk of heart disease?
6 Use the Internet to find out if dogs ever suffer from heart disease.

# CHOOSE YOUR FATS WISELY

- **Cholesterol** tests measure the amount of 'good' and 'bad' cholesterol in your blood.
- 'Bad cholesterol' is cholesterol in the blood going from the liver to be deposited in tissues and arteries.
- 'Good cholesterol' is cholesterol that has left the tissues and is going back to the liver before being excreted from the body.
- The fats you eat affect your blood cholesterol levels.
- Eating **saturated fats** (in cheese, fatty meat and chocolate) leads to more 'bad cholesterol' in your blood.
- Eating **polyunsaturated fats**, like fish oil and corn oil, lowers the levels of both good and bad cholesterol.
- **Monounsaturated** fats like canola oil are the healthiest dietary fats. They increase good and reduce bad cholesterol levels.

**TOP TIP** Polyunsaturated and monounsaturated fats are collectively called 'unsaturated fats'.

### Now try this

**c** Complete the sentences by filling in the missing words.

> unsaturated    saturated    saturated
> cholesterol    cholesterol    avoided

Cream, cheese, egg yolk, fatty meats and chocolate contain _____ fats. _____ fats raise blood _____.

Replacing saturated fats with _____ fats may reduce the amount of bad _____ in your blood.

Foods with more than 20% saturated fat are high in saturated fat and should be _____.

## Homework

7 What foods and which types of fat do you have in your fridge at home?

8 Look at the food label shown on the right. Is this a healthy product? Explain your answer.

| Nutrition Facts | | |
|---|---|---|
| Serving Size: 1/2 (20 g) | | |
| Servings per container: 2 | | |
| **Amount per serving** | | |
| Calories: 370   Calories from fat: 170 | | |
| | | % Daily Value * |
| Total fat: 19 g | | 29% |
| Saturated fat: 12 g | | 60% |
| Cholesterol: 15 mg | | 5% |
| Sodium: 250 mg | | 10% |
| Total carbohydrate: 46g | | 15% |
| Dietary fibre: 2 g | | 8% |
| Sugars: 33 g | | |

# BLOOD PRESSURE

- **Blood pressure** is the force of blood pushing against the walls of the arteries.
- Blood pressure goes up and down in everyday life and also during the heart beat cycle.
- One in three adults in the UK have **hypertension**. This means their blood pressure is high, which puts a strain on the heart and arteries.
- Hypertension is caused by several factors, for example, genetics, age and smoking.
- By reducing the amount of **sodium** we eat, we can lower our blood pressure. Sodium is found in **salt**.
- The reduction in blood pressure varies from person to person.
- In general, aim to eat less than 6 g (about one teaspoon) of table salt a day. Note that 6 g of salt contains 2.5 g of sodium.

## Homework

9 How much salt is in your diet? Visit http://www.salt.gov.uk/index.shtml

10 Foods with 1.25 g of salt per 100 g are said to be high in salt. List **five** such foods.

# How to think like a food scientist

## HOW FOOD SCIENTISTS THINK

- Food scientists work in the food industry, developing new products and improving existing products.
- Food scientists also work for the UK's Food Standards Agency where they test foods to make sure they are safe and labelled correctly.
- The Agency tests foods for: biochemical or microbiological spoilage, levels of salt, fat, potentially toxic additives, pesticides and many more things.
- The Agency's first duty is to protect the public and as new findings, ingredients and processes come to light, their advice is updated.
- Once released, this information can have a significant social and economic impact on the public and market.

### Now try this

**a** Match the items on the left-hand side with the correct test on the right-hand side.

**i** iron(III)

TEST 1 Add the indicator phenolphthalein; add drops of sodium hydroxide (a reagent). Look for a colour change.

**ii** moisture content

TEST 2 Weigh the food, heat to evaporate water, then weigh again.

**iii** acidity by titration

TEST 3 Grind food and form a solution; add colourless thiocyanate ion SCN. Look for a red colour change.

### Homework

1 Prepare a table showing qualitative tests for: starch, protein, fat, reducing sugar and acidity.
2 Visit http://www.food.gov.uk/ (Food Standards Agency). Summarise **two** public surveys that interest you.

## FOOD ADDITIVES

- The main types of **food additive** are: antioxidants, colours, emulsifiers and thickeners, flavour enhancers, preservatives and sweeteners.
- Food additives are added to foods to improve taste, texture, appearance and/or shelf life.
- The use of food additives is controlled by the EU. Each additive is tested and given an **E-number**.
- Additives are approved if test results show that consuming reasonable amounts does not produce any known adverse health effects.
- The **Acceptable Daily Intake (ADI)** of an additive is the amount that a person may eat or drink each day for an entire lifetime without causing any known harm to health.
- The same additive may be in several products. Therefore surveys are carried out to make sure that people do not regularly consume more than the ADI.
- As with many foods, individuals may be allergic to certain additives and will therefore need to avoid them.

### Homework

3 Find **five** food labels and write down the E-numbers for each category of additive.
4 What is traffic light labelling? Is it a good idea? Look at: http://www.eatwell.gov.uk/foodlabels/trafficlights/
5 Visit the interactive food label at http://www.eatwell.gov.uk/foodlabels/understandlabels/

# ANTIOXIDANTS

- **Antioxidants** help to stop fats, oils and some vitamins from reacting with oxygen in the air.
- These reactions are what make oily food taste rancid and cause vegetables to lose their colour.
- Antioxidants occur naturally in many foods (for example, tomatoes, strawberries, carrots).
- The ones added to foods are extracted or made synthetically.
- **Vitamin C (ascorbic acid**, E300) is an antioxidant and is added to soft drinks, jams and sausages.
- Antioxidants also seem to protect us from unstable molecules called **free radicals**, which can damage cells.

 **TOP TIP** Preservatives stop mould and bacteria from growing; antioxidants stop reactions with oxygen.

## Now try this

**b** Cross out one word, or part of a word, from each sentence to make it correct.

Dipping an apple slice in lemon juice stops it from going brown because there is no vitamin C in the juice.

Antioxidants stop foods from reacting with fury oxygen.

Sugar, salt and vinegar are inedible natural preservatives.

Vinegar cannot be used as a preservative and has an E-number.

## Homework

6 Do a fair test to see if lemon juice keeps a slice of apple fresh.

7 Can you find a food with an added antioxidant? What is it?

8 Read up on additives at http://www.eatwell.gov.uk/foodlabels/understandingenumbers/

# COLOURS AND ARTIFICIAL SWEETENERS

- **Artificial sweeteners** taste sweet but have few or no calories.
- **Aspartame** (which tastes 200 times sweeter than table sugar and has no calories) is digested in the body and is then broken down into **toxins** in the liver.
- Currently the Food Standards Agency approves aspartame for use, on the basis that the quantity of toxins is small.
- Colours are used to make foods look more attractive, for example, when natural colour is lost during processing.
- Some people are allergic to certain colours, such as cochineal, a natural colour extracted from insects.

- **Tartrazine** (E102) is a synthetic yellow dye used in some cordials and fizzy drinks. It is known to unsettle some hyperactive children.
- Many consumers look for foods without colours. This is because they think that colours are unnecessary and may be damaging to health.

## Now try this

**c** Give **two** advantages that sweeteners have over sugar.

**d** List the products you eat or drink that contain aspartame. How many do you consume in a day and why might this matter?

## Homework

9 Interview your parents to find out about their views on colours and artificial sweeteners.

10 Search the BBC's website and 'How Stuff Works' for articles on colours or aspartame and report on the highlights.

11 Do you avoid foods with added colours? Explain your answer.

# Keeping food safe

## FOOD POISONING

- 'Food poisoning' refers to any illness contracted by consuming contaminated food or water.
- Contaminants that cause illness are:
  - microorganisms (bacteria, viruses and fungi)
  - toxins produced by microorganisms
  - chemical contaminants (such as pesticides and metals)
  - naturally occurring (organic) toxins in some mushrooms and seafood

### Now try this

a Match these bacteria (i, ii and iii) with food sources (A, B and C) and symptoms (X, Y and Z).

| | | |
|---|---|---|
| i Clostridium botulinum | A Meat and meat products, poultry, eggs | X Respiratory problems, blurred vision, and possible death |
| ii Salmonella | B Raw or undercooked shellfish | Y Nausea, vomiting, fever, abdominal cramps and diarrhoea |
| iii Vibrio parahaemolyticus | C Improperly canned foods often home-canned | Z Diarrhoea, cramps, vomiting, headache and fever |

- Food-spoiling bacteria are the most common cause of food poisoning. For example, salmonella, campylobacter and E-Coli.

### Homework

1 Use the Internet to research a UK food scare or product recall and present your findings in a report. (Try the Food Standards Agency website.)
2 Find food labels that describe storage instructions and bring them into class.

## SLOWING AND HALTING BACTERIAL GROWTH

- Bacteria need warmth, moisture and a food source to grow.
- Large numbers of bacteria and/or their toxins must be present to cause poisoning, therefore it may be possible to prevent illness by:
  - cooking lightly contaminated foods to kill bacteria before they multiply
  - chilling food to slow down bacterial growth (bacteria grow rapidly at temperatures between 5 and 40 °C)
  - drying food
  - exercising good hygiene habits in order to prevent the contamination of uncontaminated foods
  - preserving foods in high concentrations of salt or vinegar, which are toxic for bacteria.

### Now try this

b How often can food safely be reheated after cooking and chilling?

c List five ways to stop or slow bacterial growth in food.

d Why must a wire loop be 'flamed' in a Bunsen flame before being used to streak an agar plate with bacteria?

### Homework

3 How and why do these food preservation methods work: canning, drying and pickling?
4 In the danger zone of temperature, bacteria grow rapidly. What is this zone?
5 What temperature is your fridge set to and what should it be set to?

# SALMONELLA

- **Salmonella** bacteria may be present in animal faeces.
- Foods such as raw meat and eggs can be **contaminated** through direct contact with faeces.
- Cooked foods can be contaminated if food handlers do not wash their hands after handling raw foods or after going to the toilet.
- Salmonella produces an intestinal infection and commonly leads to diarrhoea, fever and abdominal cramps.
- Symptoms may not appear until 12–24 hours after infection.
- The infection usually resolves itself within 5 to 7 days without medical treatment.

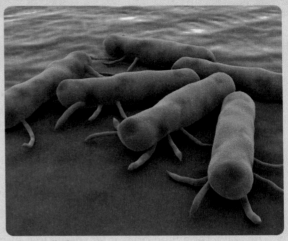

*Salmonella bacteria.*

**TOP TIP** Preparation surfaces can harbour bacteria and should be cleaned thoroughly with disinfectant before use.

## Homework

6  Write a television advertisement to warn the public about poisoning by campylobacter, E-Coli and salmonella.

7  What are the symptoms of infection by these bacteria?

8  Present a radio report about an E-Coli outbreak.

## 'USE BY' AND 'BEST BEFORE'

- It is important to store foods in the correct way and to follow any cooking, eating or storage instructions given on the label.
- A **'use by' date** is given on **perishable** foods such as meat, dairy and ready-prepared salads.
- Using the food after this date or storing it incorrectly may lead to food poisoning.
- The 'use by' date does not always mean 'eat by' because cooking or freezing a food extends its life. The consumer is then responsible for ensuring the food is safe.
- A **'best before' date** is given on frozen, dried and tinned foods. These foods may be safe to eat after this date but lose flavour and texture.
- Eggs, however, should not be eaten after the 'best before' date. Some contain salmonella bacteria which multiply over time.

**TOP TIP** We can measure the number of bacteria present in food to determine whether or not the food has been handled correctly.

### Now try this

**e** Labelling shows (tick all that apply):

| | | |
|---|---|---|
| **i** | the food's name | ☐ |
| **ii** | the ingredients | ☐ |
| **iii** | the percentage of any ingredient in the food's name | ☐ |
| **iv** | durability (best before/eat by/use by) | ☐ |
| **v** | any special storage conditions | ☐ |
| **vi** | the manufacturer | ☐ |
| **vii** | a warning about potential allergens (celery, gluten, eggs, fish, milk, mustard, nuts, sesame seeds, soya, sulfur dioxide) | ☐ |

## Homework

9   Design food labels for a fictitious chocolate dessert, giving all of the appropriate information.

10  Use the Internet to find out which food allergies are most common in Britain.

11  Draw up a table showing foods you have at home and their 'best before' dates.

# Food and farming

## USEFUL MICROBES

- **Microorganisms** are used in food production.
- The microbes break down complex molecules in the original product in order to release energy for growth.
- **Yeast** is a **fungus** which produces alcohol (ethanol) and carbon dioxide when it is fed sugar.
- In bread making, yeast is used to produce carbon dioxide. The carbon dioxide makes the bread rise.
- In wine production, yeast is added to fruit juice to produce alcohol.
- **Lactobacilli** are the bacteria which turn milk into yoghurt.
- These bacteria feed on the **lactose** sugar in milk and produce acids, which prevent other microbes from growing.
- Cheese is also made by bacteria from milk. Different bacteria produce different flavoured cheeses.

### Now try this

**a** Match each food with the appropriate microbe.

| i | cheese | bacteria |
| ii | beer | bacteria |
| iii | yoghurt | fungus |
| iv | sour cream | yeast |
| v | wine | yeast |
| vi | bread | bacteria |

 **TOP TIP** When microorganisms (bacteria, fungi or yeasts) produce a chemical change in foods, this is called fermentation.

### Homework

1  Draw a flowchart to show the steps involved in cheese production.
2  Which bacteria are used to make yoghurt?
3  What are the so-called 'good bacteria' in some foods and why are they good?

## FARMING METHODS

- Farmers manage soil and/or animals to produce food.
- As crops grow they remove **nutrients** from the soil.
- Farmers needs to replace these nutrients in order for more crops to grow in the future. Plants also need to be protected from weeds and pests.
- In **intensive farming**, farmers use manufactured **fertilisers** and **pesticides** to manage the soil.
- Intensive farming can produce large quantities of food for a relatively low cost.
- **Organic farming** avoids synthetic chemicals and relies on naturally occurring biological processes instead.
- Producing food organically takes longer, produces lower yields and therefore has a higher cost.
- The advantages of organic farming are that it leaves fewer toxic chemicals in the food, and it is less taxing on the environment.

### Now try this

**b** Match each of these terms with the correct definition:

| i | Adds nutrients to the soil. | artificial fertilisers |
| ii | Chemicals to prevent or destroy pests such as insects, mice, weeds and fungi. | herbicides |
| iii | Chemicals designed to kill weeds. | pesticides |

### Homework

4  What is the possible impact on health of eating food containing herbicides?

## ORGANIC FARMING

- Plants draw **nutrients** from the soil. These include nitrates, phosphates, potassium and magnesium.
- **Organic farmers** use traditional and natural means to replace these nutrients.
- **Manure** and **crop rotation** are used to enrich the soil with **nitrates**: growing a **leguminous crop** after the main crop puts nitrates back into the soil.
- **Pest control** is achieved by using habitat management and natural predators.
- For livestock, organic standards do not allow intensive housing of stock.
- Routine medicines (such as antibiotics and wormers) are not permitted. The aim is that animals are kept healthy using preventative care and good husbandry.

 **TOP TIP** Farming in Britain is guided by DEFRA, the Department for Environment, Food and Rural Affairs.

### Now try this

**c** Fill in the missing words.

> wildlife    food    agro-chemical
> nutritional    organic    minimise

_____ production systems are designed to produce optimum quantities of _____ of high _____ quality by using management practices which aim to avoid the use of _____ inputs and which _____ damage to the environment and _____ .

### Homework

5. Design an investigation to find out whether plants grow faster when given organic or inorganic fertilisers.
6. Is it true that garlic can keep aphids away from cabbage plants?
7. Find out how much extra you pay for **five** items of organic produce at your local supermarket.

## SAFE FOODS

- The main concerns regarding the use of **chemical pesticides** and **fertilisers** are:
  - on the farm, chemicals could potentially damage the health of those applying them, the environment and local animals
  - consumers may be affected by **chemical residues** in foods.
- There are laws regarding the amounts of pesticide residues that are allowed on foods.
- The FDA (Food Standards Agency) carries out tests to ensure levels of pesticides are within the set limits.
- The FDA also investigates concerns raised by the public, such as the impact on consumer health of eating 'cocktails' of pesticides from many sources.
- Washing and peeling vegetables can help remove residual pesticides but some residues are systemic (inside the vegetable).

### Now try this

**d** Spelling check: circle the words that are spelt correctly.

| | |
|---|---|
| addative | fertalise |
| pestiside | pesticide |
| additive | fertilise |
| flavouring | preservitave |
| preservative | bacterea |
| bacteria | bactera |

### Homework

8. Print out and summarise an article from newscientist.com about pesticides.
9. Hold a family conference about whether to 'go organic' and report on the highlights.
10. Design the layout and headings for a three page website about food science.

# Sports science basics

## THE WINNING EDGE

- Today's top athletes benefit from the help of sports scientists.
- Physiologists know about the body and help athletes achieve optimum fitness.
- Fitness training improves the performance of key organs such as the heart and lungs as well as muscles.
- Nutritionists understand diet and help athletes eat the right foods.
- Materials scientists research the properties of materials. They give advice about clothes and equipment.
- Psychologists focus on how people think and help athletes prepare themselves mentally.

### Now try this

**a** Link each item with the sports scientist who studies it.

| | |
|---|---|
| Cardiovascular system | nutritionist |
| Isotonic sports drinks | physiologist |
| Aerodynamics | nutritionist |
| High protein diet | materials scientist |

 **TOP TIP** Sports scientists research and apply scientific principles to help athletes improve their performance.

## Homework

1 Think up **ten** questions that a psychologist, nutritionist and materials scientist might ask in their work.
2 Review the sports science section at the Exploratorium website. What's your top pick?

## THE CARDIOVASCULAR SYSTEM

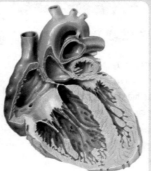

- The **cardiovascular system** consists of the heart (as pump), arteries, veins, capillaries and blood.
- The cardiovascular system transports food and oxygen to cells and carries carbon dioxide and waste products away.
- The heart has four **chambers**.
- **Deoxygenated blood** from the body enters the right **atrium**, then the right **ventricle**, then heads out to the lungs to get oxygen and back to the heart.
- **Oxygenated blood** enters the left atrium, then the left ventricle and is then pumped into the aorta and on to the body.

### Now try this

**b** Describe how the cardiovascular system carries glucose to muscles using words like: glucose, red blood cells, small intestine, insulin, muscle.

_____

_____

_____

_____

_____

_____

_____

_____

## Homework

3 Watch an animation of the heart such as the one at: http://www.schoolscience.co.uk/content/4/biology/abpi/heart/heartAnim3.html
4 Draw and label the journey of a red blood cell moving through the cardiovascular system.
5 Explain how valves control the movement of blood.

# CHANGES WHEN EXERCISING

- We breathe to supply our cells with a steady supply of oxygen and to expel carbon dioxide.
- The **thorax** (or thoracic cavity) consists of the body parts inside the rib cage, below the neck and above the **diaphragm**.
- The diaphragm is a sheet of muscles at the bottom of the ribcage.
- When you **inhale** (breath in), your diaphragm moves down, your ribs expand and this sucks air into your lungs.
- When you **exhale** (breathe out) the diaphragm moves up and the rib cage moves in – which pushes air out.
- During exercise, the breathing rate increases to supply more oxygen to muscles.

 **Gas exchange** refers to the way that oxygen moves from air to blood while carbon dioxide moves from blood to air.

### Now try this.

c Describe the journey of air into the lungs by inserting the missing words into the following sentences.

bronchi    trachea    alveoli

Air travels down the _____, through the _____ (there are two) and into the bronchioles inside the lungs. The bronchioles lead to millions of tiny sacs called _____.

## Homework

6  How many breaths per minute do you or a friend take at rest?

7  How many do you or a friend take when jogging on the spot?

8  Draw and label the body parts involved in breathing.

# RESPIRATION

- Cells contain tiny rods called **mitochondria**. These 'power houses' convert glucose into energy. This is called **respiration**.
- In **aerobic respiration**, energy is released from **glucose** in the presence of **oxygen**.
- In **anaerobic respiration**, oxygen is not present. The glucose is only partially broken down, releasing less energy and **lactic acid**.
- During heavy exercise, oxygen supply can't keep up and muscle cells respire anaerobically.
- A build up of lactic acid leads to muscle pain. After exercise the lactic acid is broken down using oxygen and is converted to carbon dioxide and water.

mitochondrion    cytoplasm

nucleus

nucleolus

### Now try this

d Write the equation for aerobic respiration.

_____

_____

e Write the equation for anaerobic respiration.

_____

_____

 The **oxygen debt** is the extra oxygen needed to break down lactic acid.

## Homework

9   Find out the percentages of oxygen and carbon dioxide present in the air we inhale and exhale.

10  Which athletes are more likely to respire anaerobically – sprinters or marathon runners? Why?

11  Why do athletes go to sites at high altitudes to train?

# Exercise and the body

## KEEPING COOL

- Our normal body temperature is 37 °C. Overheating stops enzymes in the body from working properly.
- Active muscles produce heat, which needs to be removed.
- Temperature regulation (**thermoregulation**) happens in these three ways:
  - hairs on the skin lie down to let air move freely and carry away heat
  - glands in the skin produce sweat, which **evaporates** drawing heat from the body
  - blood capillaries just under the skin **dilate** to bring more blood near to the body surface to cool. This is called **vasodilation**.

 The **hypothalamus** in the brain monitors body temperature.

### Now try this

**a** What are capillaries?

_____

_____

_____

_____

**b** How are capillaries involved in thermoregulation?

_____

_____

_____

### Homework

1 What is heatstroke, why does it happen and what should you do?
2 Prepare a poster to warn athletes about heat exhaustion or heatstroke.
3 Use the Internet to find out about sweat and/or antiperspirants.

## WATER REGULATION

- Water from food and drink enters the blood. Water is lost via breathing, sweating, urine and faeces.
- The **hypothalamus** controls the level of water in the blood. This is called **osmoregulation**.
- If the hypothalamus detects that there is too little water in the blood, it signals the **pituitary gland** to release the hormone **ADH**.
- ADH tells the kidneys to stop removing water from the blood.
- If the hypothalamus detects too much water, it tells the pituitary gland to stop releasing ADH.
- The kidneys work harder, removing more water.

 The pituitary gland is the size of a pea and secretes many hormones.

### Now try this

**c** The master control for the pituitary is the hypothalamus.

True or false? _____

**d** What happens to cells if the blood becomes too watery?

_____

**e** How does urine change when the body is short of water?

_____

_____

### Homework

4 List **five** bodily processes controlled by the pituitary gland.
5 Which of these body parts are involved in osmoregulation: kidneys, blood, hypothalamus, pituitary gland?

# BLOOD GLUCOSE REGULATION

- After eating, **glucose** enters the bloodstream. Between meals there is no supply.
- Cells need a steady supply of glucose so blood sugar levels need to be controlled.
- This is achieved by the release of the hormones **insulin** and **glucagon**.
- After eating, **beta cells** in the pancreas release insulin, which helps muscle and tissue cells take glucose from the blood.
- Insulin also triggers the liver to take up glucose and store it as **glycogen**.
- If the blood sugar level becomes low, insulin release stops.
- Instead, **alpha cells** in the pancreas produce the hormone glucagon.
- Glucagon instructs the liver to convert glycogen to glucose – restoring blood sugar.

### Now try this

**f** Which cells release insulin?

_____

**g** Which cells release glucagon?

_____

**h** What are the islets of Langerhans?

_____

 **TOP TIP** The control of blood sugar is called **glucoregulation**.

## Homework

6 Summarise the processes of glucoregulation, osmoregulation and thermoregulation.

7 What are the symptoms if blood sugar gets **a)** abnormally high and **b)** abnormally low?

8 Draw the pancreas and stomach and label them.

# MUSCLES

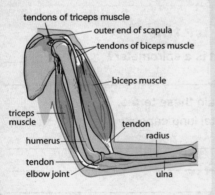

tendons of triceps muscle
outer end of scapula
tendons of biceps muscle
biceps muscle
triceps muscle
tendon
radius
humerus
tendon
elbow joint
ulna

- **Muscles** can **contract** but they cannot **stretch** by themselves.
- For this reason, all muscles work in pairs: when one muscle contracts, this stretches (relaxes) the other.
- In the case of the arm, the **biceps** (on top) contract to bend the elbow and pull up the lower arm.
- This stretches the **triceps** – the muscle on the back of the arm.
- To straighten the arm, the triceps contracts, stretching the biceps and pulling the arm down.

### Now try this

**i** What joins muscles to bones – tendons or veins?

_____

**j** Which leg muscle forms an antagonistic pair with the quadriceps?

_____

**k** What is the insertion of a muscle?

_____

_____

_____

_____

## Homework

9 Why is it important to warm up before running?

10 Explain how an athlete might tear a hamstring.

11 Watch the biceps in action on the BBC 'humanbody' site:
http://www.bbc.co.uk/science/humanbody/body/factfiles/workinpairs/biceps_animation.shtml

# Physiological changes

## PHYSIOLOGY

- Physiologists study the functions of organs and organ systems in the body.
- Physiological changes are changes that happen to these functions.
- Sports physiologists focus on how the functions of the body change during training and competition.
- They take **baseline measurements** of **heart rate**, **breathing rate** and temperature before exercise. They compare these with measurements taken during exercise and after exercise.
- This information is used to design an appropriate fitness program for the athlete and to monitor changes in fitness levels.

 **TOP TIP** Heart rate can be measured using a electrocardiograph, which produces a graphical representation of how the rate changes during an exercise session.

### Now try this

**a** Identify each of the following measurements as **observational (O)**, **physiological (P)** or **subjective (S)**.

Videotaping an athlete diving to measure angle of entry into water. ☐

Measuring the amount of lactic acid building up in the blood. ☐

Asking the athlete how she feels after a new training program. ☐

Measuring oxygen consumption and heart rate during a treadmill run. ☐

### Homework

1 Why is it useful to measure the build up of lactic acid in the blood?
2 Use the Internet to find out what is taught on a university sports science course.
3 Use the Internet to find out what sports physiology is concerned with. Summarise your findings.

## MEASURING HEART RATE AND LUNG CAPACITY

- A typical 'resting' **heart rate** is 70 **beats per minute** (bpm) for men and 75 beats per minute for women.
- Heart rate is usually lower for athletes and higher for obese people.
- Heart rate increases during exercise (to about 180 bpm depending on age) and then falls again when resting.
- **Heart rate recovery** is a measure of how much the heart rate falls in the first minute after peak exercise.
- The heart rate gradually returns to its normal beat.
- The healthier and fitter a person's heart is, the more quickly this happens.

 **TOP TIP** Baseline data are measurements made before training. They are used to monitor improvements in performance and recovery after injury.

### Now try this

**b** What is a spirometer? _____

_____

**c** Explain these terms:

  **i** total lung capacity

_____

_____

_____

  **ii** tidal capacity

_____

_____

_____

### Homework

4 Use a PowerPoint demonstration to describe how to measure:
- heart rate and breathing rate before and during exercise
- vital and tidal volume of lungs using a spirometer.

## MEASURING GLUCOSE AND GRIP

- A **dipstick** is used to discover the strength of various substances, for example, glucose levels in urine or blood.
- Dipsticks are kept in air-tight containers. The **reagent** areas must not be touched during the test.
- After dipping in the liquid, excess liquid is blotted off the strip to prevent mixing between pads.
- The reagent pads must be read at the specified times. The colours are compared with a colour chart.
- One source of error is discolouration by the test liquid, which can produce false results.

 To increase a test's accuracy, take repeat measurements.

### Now try this

**d** What is a dynamometer?

_____

_____

**e** Would you expect the same grip strength with each hand?

_____

**f** How could you use a dynamometer to monitor improvement in performance?

_____

_____

_____

### Homework

5  Create a PowerPoint presentation showing how to use a dipstick.

6  Find pictures on the Internet of a dynamometer. How does it work?

7  Describe **four** techniques used to measure physiological changes during exercise.

## PERSONALISING THE PROGRAM

- Sports scientists develop individual diet and fitness programs for top athletes. They design these to suit the physiology of the athlete and the sport.
- Most athletes require several hundred **kilocalories** of additional energy every day when training and competing.
- Without this additional energy, there may be a breakdown of muscle and bone over time, and therefore a greater chance of injuries.
- A healthy **balanced diet** containing fruit, vegetables and plenty of carbohydrates (the main energy source for exercise) is vital.
- For some sports, a low body mass is advantageous. Athletes keep their body fat low by restricting their calorie intake.
- Some athletes eat high protein diets, believing this will build muscle size. There is some debate about whether this strategy works.
- Teenage athletes need a higher proportion of protein in their diets and additional energy proportional to their body mass for growth.

### Now try this

**g** Fill in the missing words.

endurance    athlete    muscles
diet    complex carbohydrates
glycogen

Carb-loading is often carried out by athletes before _____ events. In the days leading up to the event, the _____ switches to a _____ that is very high in

_____

(pasta, potatoes, rice and bread) to build up _____ stores in the _____.

### Homework

8  Use the Internet to devise effective diets for **three** athletes doing different sports.

9  List **eight** dietary recommendations for teenage athletes.

# Nutrition

## ENERGY NEEDS

- We need **energy** to live, to grow, to move, to repair and to keep warm.
- When the energy gained from food is greater than the energy used, the excess is stored as fat.
- The **body mass index (BMI)** indicates whether an individual's weight falls within a healthy range, based on their height.
- The basic idea is that the more body fat an individual has, the higher their BMI.
- $BMI = \dfrac{\text{weight in kg}}{(\text{height in m})^2}$
- A healthy BMI is in the range of 20–25; a BMI of over 30 indicates **obesity**.
- Muscle is more dense than fat, so athletes may have a high BMI but still be healthy.

### Now try this

**a** What is the equation used to calculate a person's BMI?

**b** What do these ranges of BMI indicate about someone's weight?

  **i** a BMI of below 19

  _____

  **ii** a BMI of 20–24

  _____

  **iii** a BMI of 25–30

  _____

### Homework

1 Use the Internet to find an online BMI calculator and work out your BMI.

2 The standard BMI ranges do not apply to pregnant women, the frail and children. Why?

3 What are the health risks associated with being underweight and overweight?

## BASIC ENERGY REQUIREMENTS

- Our daily energy needs vary depending on our body mass, age, exercise level and ambient temperature.
- The **basic energy requirement (BER)** is the amount of energy needed for an adult of a specified weight in a normal day.
- BER = 1.3 kcals × (weight in kg) × 24 hrs
- The greater your weight, the higher your BER.
- The **personal energy requirement (PER)** of an athlete is their basic energy requirement plus the extra energy needed for training and competing.
- The extra energy needed depends on exercise intensity, duration and the weight of the athlete.

 **TOP TIP** Energy needs increase during the years of growth: boys aged 15 to 18 need about 2755 kcals a day; girls aged 15 to 18 need about 2110 kcals a day.

### Now try this

**c** What is the BER of a lightweight rower who weighs 50 kg? _____

**d** If the rower uses an extra 800 kcals a day during training, what is his PER? _____

**e** Complete this paragraph:

To run a marathon, a runner may require an extra 3000–5000 kcals of _____. To provide this, the athlete burns _____ in addition to using glycogen.

### Homework

4 Use the Internet to search for **ten** top diet tips for athletes.

5 Search the Internet for information on sporting physiques.

6 Find out the estimated BERs for a sprinter and weightlifter. Explain what your answer means.

# RAISING AND RESTORING ENERGY LEVELS

- Before exercising, athletes may 'load up on carbs' to ensure that their **glycogen** stores are filled.
- In training and competition, an athlete draws on these glycogen stores for energy.
- In endurance events, athletes also draw on **fat** stores.
- After an event, athletes may eat foods with a high **GI (Glycaemic Index)** to restore their glycogen levels quickly so they are ready for their next event.
- The GI indicates how much and how quickly a food raises **blood glucose levels**.
- **Glucose** has a very high GI and provides energy quickly.

**TOP TIP** Sports nutritionists use food composition tables to plan athletes' meals in order to ensure the energy and nutrient intakes are correct.

## Now try this

**f** What is a kilocalorie (kcal) and what is a kilojoule (kJ)?

_____

_____

**g** Brown bread has 220 kcal per 100 g, 45 g of carbohydrates and 2 g of fat. Is it high in fat?

_____

**h** Avocados have 220 kcal per 100 g, 2 g of carbohydrates and 20 g of fat. Are they high in fat?

_____

## Homework

7   Find a food composition table and copy out the values for protein, carbohydrates, fat and energy for **ten** different types of food.

8   Which of the foods in your table do you find surprising and why?

9   Put stars by the foods that are particularly low in fat and high in carbohydrates.

# ISOTONIC DRINKS

- **Isotonic drinks** contain water, glucose and **electrolytes**.
- Water, lost through sweating, needs to be replaced.
- Glucose restores an athlete's glycogen stores and provides a rapid energy boost.
- The amount of glucose in these drinks is between 6 and 8%. At this level, fluid leaves the stomach and enters the system quickly.
- **Hypertonic drinks** are higher in glucose but leave the stomach more slowly. They are consumed after exercise but not during it.
- Electrolytes are charged particles that are used by cells.
- Electrolytes – particularly sodium and potassium – are lost in sweat and need to be replaced.

## Now try this

**i** Match the deficiencies on the left-hand side with the appropriate symptoms (**A, B** or **C**) on the right-hand side.

| dehydration | **A** Sweating, shaking, extreme hunger, dizziness, headache |
| sodium deficiency | **B** Fatigue, loss of concentration, and ultimately heatstroke |
| low blood sugar | **C** Muscle weakness, cramps and nausea |

## Homework

10   List the ingredients of an isotonic drink – search the Internet or your local shop.

11   Explain why the following ingredients are included in this homemade isotonic drink: 200 ml of concentrated orange squash, 1 litre of water and a pinch of salt.

12   How could you vary the recipe above to produce a hypertonic drink?

# Materials for sport

## DRESSED FOR SUCCESS

- Material scientists design equipment, footwear and clothing for athletes.
- Their aim is to find designs and materials that can improve an athlete's performance.
- For sports such as ice-speed racing and bicycling:
  - helmets and clothing need to minimise air resistance
  - footwear needs to be lightweight and strong.
- For racket sports like squash and tennis:
  - clothes need to keep the athlete cool and not restrict blood circulation
  - footwear needs to be lightweight and provide good grip
  - racquets need to be strong and light.

 **TOP TIP** Tests in wind tunnels show that smooth, shiny fabrics create the least resistance.

### Now try this

a Which of these aspects of sport do material scientists look at: clothes, footwear, nutrition, sports surfaces, equipment?

_____

_____

b Polyester T-shirts and vests for sport are designed to draw moisture away from the skin – how and why?

_____

_____

## Homework

1 Search the Internet for information about the development of shoes for sport. Summarise your findings.
2 List all the clothes and equipment employed by a speed skater and pole vaulter in action.
3 What properties (for example, lightweight) are desirable for each item in your list for question 2?

## NATURAL OR SYNTHETIC?

- Traditionally, sports equipment was made from natural materials such as wood, rubber and gut.
- Now the choice is wider because of new **synthetic** materials.
- Tennis rackets used to be made from (natural) ash or maple.
- New rackets are often hollow shells made from carbon-fibre-reinforced **composites**.
- In the case of the tennis racket, this means a larger racket head for no more weight and so a larger sweet spot.
- Sportswear can also be made from natural or synthetic fibres. T-shirts can be made from cotton, a natural fibre found in cotton plants.
- They can also be made from nylon, which is a high-strength, resilient synthetic fibre produced from petroleum.

 **TOP TIP** The sweet spot of a racket is a central area which gives minimum shock to the player and minimum vibration to the ball on impact.

### Now try this

c Match the materials on the left-hand side with the correct descriptions.

hardwood    i Strong, natural material used for bats and hockey sticks

nylon    ii Tough material used for Baseball gloves and footballs

leather    iii Fibrous, strong and water resistant material used for ropes, tennis racket strings and toothbrush bristles

## Homework

4 Write a newspaper article about nylon – its manufacture, uses and properties.
5 What are the properties of natural leather and how is it treated for use in sports?

## CLOTHING CHOICES

- **Fibres** are long threads of material that can be woven to make a **fabric**.
- Natural fibres come from plants and animals. Examples are cotton and linen, which come from plants, and silk, which is made by silkworms.
- **Synthetic** fibres are produced in laboratories by drawing out long 'threads' of plastic. Examples are polyester, nylon and lycra.
- Cotton feels cool but becomes heavier as it absorbs sweat. Polyester, lycra and nylon absorb little water, so stay light and dry.
- Synthetic fabrics are generally cheaper, more lightweight, easier to dye and harder-wearing than natural materials.
- On the downside, synthetic fabrics are made from petroleum (crude oil) and natural gas – which are limited resources.

### Now try this

**d** Fill in the gaps using these words:

outdoor    perspiration    perspiration
    mesh    nylon    wind-resistant

_____ was one of the first synthetic fibres. The finely woven fabric was light and durable but trapped _____.

Many of today's garments have an inner layer of polyester, which is woven into a _____. This draws _____ outwards.

For _____ clothing, an outer layer of nylon adds a _____ shield.

### Homework

6  Search the Internet to find out what you can about bicycle shorts.

7  What is chamois and why was it once used as a lining in bicycle shorts?

8  Write a script for a TV advertisement for a new brand of lycra bicycle shorts.

## GROUPING: MATERIALS

- Solid materials can be grouped according to their molecular structures and properties (irrespective of whether they are natural or synthetic).
- Four useful groupings are **polymers**, **ceramics**, **metals** and **composites**.
- Polymers are long chains containing repeating patterns of atoms.
- Natural polymers include cotton, wool, starch, natural rubber and plant cellulose.
- Synthetic polymers are commonly called **plastics** and include polystyrene, polyester, and nylon.
- Polymers can form **fibres** if the chains are stretched out, or rubbery materials if the chains are left tangled.
- Generally, polymers are light, flexible and have a low thermal conductivity.

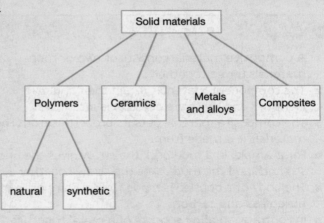

 **TOP TIP** Natural materials can often be treated to change their properties and make them more useful.

### Homework

9   Define the terms ceramic, polymer, synthetic and natural.

10  Search the Internet to find out about the uses and properties of GORE-TEX®.

11  Compare the properties of artificial grass and natural grass.

# Metals and composites

## METALS

- **Metals** are mined from the ground.
- They are generally shiny, hard, flexible, good conductors of heat and electricity, and have high tensile strength.
- Iron, copper and gold are **dense**. The shot put is made from solid cast iron.
- Aluminium and titanium are lighter but still strong. They are used for bicycle frames, golf clubs, tennis rackets, and wheelchairs for sport.
- Steel is an **alloy** of iron. It is made by adding carbon to iron in order to strengthen it.
- Steel is strong and flexible and is used to make facemasks to protect fencers and american footballers.
- The handles of badminton rackets are made from hollow steel – making them light and strong.

### Now try this

**a** What is a ferrous metal?

_____
_____

**b** What were heads of golf clubs originally made from?

_____

**c** What are heads of golf clubs made from now?

_____

### Homework

1. Give **four** examples of alloys and explain how they are made.
2. Search the Internet to find out the densities of **ten** metals and alloys in SI units.
3. Summarise the properties and uses of each metal in a table.

## COMPOSITES

- A **composite** material consists of two or more materials mixed together.
- The component materials retain their original identities and there are detectable interfaces.
- The composite material gets its properties from the materials it is made from.
- For example, in a mud brick the straw gives the brick strength and the mud cakes the straw together.
- The body of a bobsled is made from a composite of **fibreglass** and **carbon**.
- In contrast, an **alloy** consists of a metal together with one or more additional elements.
- In the case of the alloy, the elements form **bonds** at an atomic level. The alloy is a new material with metallic properties.

### Now try this

**d** Decide which of these materials are **composites (C)** and which are **alloys (A)**.

Plywood (wood strips and adhesive) ☐

Steel (iron and carbon) ☐

Fibreglass (glass fibres and resin) ☐

Brass (zinc and copper) ☐

Pewter (tin and copper) ☐

Carbon-carbon (graphite and carbon fibres) ☐

### Homework

4. Draw labelled pictures of **two** sports people. One prefers traditional materials and one prefers composites.
5. Find out more about bobsleds and present your findings using PowerPoint.

## COMPOSITES IN ACTION

- The modern pole used in pole vaulting is a great example of materials science at work.
- Scientists tested a range of materials, lengths and shapes to find the best design.
- Their goal was to minimise weight and optimise stiffness and strength.
- In the past, the pole was made of bamboo, then aluminium and now it consists of three layers of **composites**.
- The innermost layer is **fibreglass** – a composite whose components are glass fibres and glue.
- The outer layers are a **carbon** composite consisting of carbon fibres with **epoxy resin**.
- Compared with steel, composites are stronger but are a fraction of the weight.

 **TOP TIP** The stresses on a bending pole are on the outer surfaces. This means the pole needs a strong skin but can be hollow to reduce weight.

## Homework

6 Read the article on the How Stuff Works website on the pole vault.

7 Draw and label the structure of today's pole vaulting pole.

8 Create a PowerPoint presentation describing the journey from bamboo to metal to composite poles.

## PROPERTIES OF MATERIALS

- When testing a range of materials there are several properties that materials scientists frequently look at:
  - **strength**: the ability to stand up to an applied force without breaking, bending or deforming
  - **flexibility**: the ability to be flexed and bowed repeatedly without cracking or breaking
  - **tensile strength**: the ability to stretch without breaking
  - **conductivity**: the ability to conduct heat or electrical energy
  - **hardness**: the ability to resist being scratched
  - **durability**: the ability to withstand wear, especially by weathering.

 **TOP TIP** There are lots of revision sites for this topic – search 'properties of materials' then be choosy about the source and level.

### Now try this:

**e** Insert the correct words and phrases into these sentences. Choose from:

low densities    smoother surfaces
good thermal insulation    track athletes
cyclists    swimmers and bobsledders
mountain climbers and deep-sea divers

Choosing fabrics with _____ reduces the total mass of the athlete's clothing. This can lead to faster speeds and less fatigue for _____.

Choosing materials that have _____ reduces air or water resistance and hence increases speed for _____.

Choosing materials that offer _____ helps maintain body temperature. This is desirable for _____.

## Homework

9 How would you measure the density, flexibility and smoothness of **three** sample materials?

10 What are the desirable properties of the material used to make javelins?

11 Describe the materials that have been used to make javelins and why.

# Exam-style questions

1. The table shows some effects of smoking on the body. Match the words **A**, **B**, **C** and **D** with the statements **1–4** in the table.

   **A** Carbon monoxide    **B** Tar
   **C** Nicotine    **D** Smoke particles    [1]

   | Effect on the body | |
   | --- | --- |
   | 1 | reduces the amount of oxygen carried in the blood |
   | 2 | causes coughing |
   | 3 | causes cancer |
   | 4 | is addictive |

2. Different organs in the body contain different kinds of receptors. Match the parts of the body **A**, **B**, **C** and **D** with the statements **1–4** in the table.

   **A** Ears    **B** Eyes    **C** Skin    **D** Nose    [1]

   | Receptors | |
   | --- | --- |
   | 1 | contains receptors for temperature and pressure |
   | 2 | contains sound and balance receptors |
   | 3 | contains light receptors |
   | 4 | contains receptors for chemicals |

3. The passage below describes the sequence of events that occur during a reflex action. Match the words **A**, **B**, **C** and **D** with the spaces **1–4** in the sentences.

   **A** effector    **B** motor neurone
   **C** sensory neurone    **D** receptors    [1]

   Stimuli are detected by __1__ in the sense organs. Nerve impulses are carried to the CNS by a __2__. A __3__ carries the nerve impulse back to the __4__ to bring about a response.

4. Below are some data collected to show the average number of different lichen species growing on tree barks at different distances from a city centre.

   | Distance from city centre (km) | Average number of lichen species in given area |
   | --- | --- |
   | 8 | 0 |
   | 12 | 5 |
   | 16 | 10 |
   | 20 | 25 |
   | 24 | 40 |
   | 32 | 40 |

   Which of the following statements about the data in the table is true?

   A Lichens only grow in the city centre.

   B The number of lichen species increases as you move out of the city centre.

   C The number of lichen species decreases as you move out of the city centre.

   D The distance from the city centre does not affect the number of lichen species.    [1]

5. The Earth's climate is affected by human activities. Match the words **A**, **B**, **C** and **D** to the spaces **1–4** in the sentences below.

   **A** carbon dioxide    **B** deforestation
   **C** fossil fuels    **D** global warming

   When humans burn __1__ large amounts of __2__ are released into the atmosphere. __3__ also increases the amount of carbon dioxide in the atmosphere. An increased amount of carbon dioxide in the atmosphere causes __4__.    [1]

6. Explain why it is not a good idea to drive after drinking alcohol.    [2]

7. Explain how deforestation may contribute to global warming.    [4]

8. Describe three ways in which a limestone quarry might have a negative impact on the environment.    [3]

1. Match the words **A**, **B**, **C** and **D** with the spaces **1–4** in the sentences.

   **A** atom    **B** nucleus
   **C** electrons    **D** elements

   All atoms have a central __1__ which is surrounded by __2__. There are about 100 different __3__, each of which is made of one type of __4__ only.    [1]

2. Match the words **A**, **B**, **C**, and **D** with the labels **1–4** on the diagram.

   **A** polymerisation    **B** fractional distillation
   **C** combustion    **D** cracking    [1]

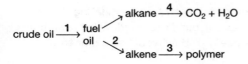

crude oil $\xrightarrow{1}$ fuel oil

fuel oil $\xrightarrow{2}$ alkene $\xrightarrow{3}$ polymer

alkane $\xrightarrow{4}$ $CO_2 + H_2O$

**3** Which of these is NOT a use for limestone?

A Reducing copper oxide to obtain copper

B Making slaked lime for neutralising acidity in soils

C Making glass

D Making mortar for use in building [1]

**4** Pick the correct ending to this statement.

Vegetable oils are unsaturated...

A this means that all of the carbon–carbon bonds are single bonds.

B this means they contain carbon–carbon bonds like those in ethene.

C you can show this by reacting them with a group 1 metal.

D they cannot be hardened to make margarine. [1]

**5** Pick the correct ending to this statement.

The Earth's atmosphere...

A is rather like the atmospheres of Jupiter and Mars today.

B has much less carbon dioxide now than it did originally.

C used to contain large amounts of ammonia and oxygen.

D has shown a decrease in carbon dioxide levels over the past 100 years. [1]

**6** Ores are obtained by quarrying.

a Explain what you understand by the term 'ore'. [1]

b Not everyone would think that having a quarry near them was a bad idea. Give one advantage of having a quarry nearby and two disadvantages. [3]

**[Total 4 marks]**

**7** Iron oxide is reduced to iron in a blast furnace. The iron made in this way has 4 % impurities.

a What problem do these impurities cause if left in the iron? [1]

b Most iron is made into alloys. What is an alloy? [1]

c What is the advantage of the alloy 'high carbon steel'? [1]

**[Total 3 marks]**

**8** Many food additives are found in food that we buy.

a Give two reasons why additives may be added to our food. [2]

b Chromatography can be used to see what particular colourings have been added to food. Describe how you would see if some of the green colouring found in some frozen peas contains the yellow colouring, tartrazine. [4]

**[Total 6 marks]**

## Physics P1a and P1b

**1** Match the words **A**, **B**, **C** and **D** with the spaces **1–4** in the sentences below.

**A** light          **B** chemical

**C** uranium      **D** kinetic (movement)

In a nuclear power station, the fuel used is ___1___.

A wind turbine changes the ___2___ energy of the wind into electrical energy.

In a remote farm, a solar panel changes ___3___ energy into electrical energy.

The battery in a DVD remote changes ___4___ energy into electrical energy. [1]

**2** The speed of electromagnetic waves is given by the equation:

$$\text{speed} = \text{wavelength} \times \text{frequency}$$

a Which of the following waves is not an electromagnetic wave?

A gamma rays

B X-rays

C radio waves

D sound [1]

b The speed of all electromagnetic waves is $3.0 \times 10^8$ m/s. What is the frequency of microwaves of wavelength 0.02 m?

A $6.0 \times 10^6$ Hz

B $3.0 \times 10^8$ Hz

C $1.5 \times 10^{10}$ Hz

D $6.7 \times 10^{-11}$ Hz [1]

**3** These questions are to do with the Universe.

a How do we know that the Universe is expanding?

A There are stars in the sky.

B The Earth's rotation gives us day and night.

C Our Solar System is expanding.

D All galaxies are moving away from each other. [1]

b What does 'red shift' mean?
A The light from a star moving away becomes longer in wavelength.
B The light from all stars becomes red.
C The light from a star moving towards us becomes shorter in wavelength.
D The Sun turns red during sunset. [1]

4 Smoke detectors use americium that emits alpha particles.
a What are alpha particles?
A electrons
B helium nuclei
C protons
D gamma rays [1]
b Which of the following statements is true about alpha particles?
A They are the least ionising radiation.
B They can only be stopped by lead of several metres thick.
C They can be deflected by a magnetic field.
D They travel at the speed of light. [1]

5 For a particular electric motor, 50 J of the electrical energy is transformed into 24 J of kinetic energy.
a Explain why the kinetic energy is not equal to the electrical energy. [1]
b Use the equation:

$$\text{efficiency} = \frac{\text{output useful energy}}{\text{total input energy}}$$

to calculate the efficiency of the motor. [3]
[Total 4 marks]

6 Cobalt-60 has a half-life of about 5.0 years and it emits gamma rays.
a Describe one difference and one similarity between gamma rays and X-rays. [2]
b Explain what is meant by 'half-life' of an isotope. [1]
c Explain how gamma rays are used in the treatment of cancer. [2]
[Total 5 marks]

## Forensic science

1 When the forensic team arrive at a crime scene they must make sure that contamination does not occur.
a Give two ways in which they make sure they do not contaminate the scene themselves. [2]
b Give one way in which they prevent the public from contaminating the scene. [1]
[Total 3 marks]

2 The forensic team are investigating the white painted surround of a window for fingerprints. Describe how they would go about this. [2]

3 A shoe print has been found at the scene of a crime.
a Give three pieces of evidence that can be gained directly from a shoe print. [3]
b Give one piece of evidence that could be worked out indirectly from the shoe size. [1]
[Total 4 marks]

4 Match the formulae to the names of these molecules by drawing a line to join them up.

| | |
|---|---|
| $C_2H_5OH$ | glucose |
| $CO_2$ | water |
| $H_2O$ | ethanol |
| $C_6H_{12}O_6$ | carbon dioxide |

[2]

5 Some tests are carried out on some chemicals. Identify the ion present from the results of the test.

| Results of test | Ion present |
|---|---|
| gives a lilac flame | |
| forms a rusty brown precipitate when sodium hydroxide solution is added | |
| forms a blue precipitate when sodium hydroxide solution is added | |
| forms a white precipitate when first nitric acid, then silver nitrate is added | |
| forms a white precipitate when first hydrochloric acid, then barium chloride solution is added | |
| fizzes vigorously when dilute hydrochloric acid is added | |

[6]

6 A sample of glass has been found at the scene of a crime.
a The forensic scientist on the assignment is new and is not sure how to find the refractive index of the glass. Write a set of instructions to explain what he must do. [4]
b Some blood is found on the glass. What three pieces of information can be obtained from this sample of blood? [3]
[Total 7 marks]

## Food science

1. 17-year-old Jesse Martin sailed solo around the world. Before setting out, he stored enough food on board for the whole journey with the help of Jacinta Oxford, a nutritionist.

A typical day's food consisted of: milk, cereal, dried fruit, chew bars, cheese, freeze-dried meat and vegetables.

Here are the valuable nutrients that are in each of these foods. Cross out the nutrient from each food that is not present in large amounts. [4]

| a | milk | vitamin A | calcium | fibre | protein |
|---|---|---|---|---|---|
| b | cereal | carbohydrates | calcium | fibre | protein |
| c | dried fruit | salt | vitamin C | fibre | carbohydrates |
| d | meat | zinc | calcium | fat | protein |

e Jesse needed to eat about 5000 kilocalories a day. Most young men his age need about 2200 kilocalories. Why did Jesse need more? [2]

f Jesse snacked on dried fruit. In the past, sailors had no access to any kind of fruit or vegetables while at sea. What nutrient did their diet lack? [1]

g What role does this nutrient play in the body? [2]

h Why was the fruit dried and not fresh? [1]

i What other essential nutrient that is not listed here did Jesse undoubtedly consume? [1]

j Do you think Jesse's daily diet was balanced? Why or why not? [2]

**[Total 13 marks]**

2. A book called 'A better guide to healthy living' begins with a list of ten tips. Tip three says that putting table sugar on cereal is 'a waste of calories' and that slices of apple are a healthier sweetener.

a Why does this author think that sugar is a 'waste of calories'? [2]

b Name two valuable nutrients that the apple can provide. [2]

c The sweet taste of sugar comes from a sugar molecule called sucrose. During digestion this is changed to glucose and carried around the body in the blood. How does the body use glucose? [2]

d The sweet taste of an apple comes from two types of sugar molecule – fructose and glucose. Glucose moves quickly from the intestine into the blood. What happens to the fructose? [2]

e Would you survive if you cut out white sugar totally from your diet? Explain your answer. [3]

f The amount of sugar in the blood is controlled by two hormones, insulin and glucagon. What happens if the blood sugar level becomes very high after a sugary snack? [3]

**[Total 14 marks]**

3. Sarah and Joe have decided that from now on they will only grow organic food on their farm. Tick the statements that are true.

From now on:

A They must not use any artificial pesticides to kill pests.

B They cannot water the plants – they must wait for natural rain.

C They will need to find a natural way to fertilise the soil such as manure.

D They will probably get a lower yield than previously from each field.

E There will be fewer toxic chemicals in the soil after the harvest.

F They will need to sell the food at a lower cost to the supermarkets. [1]

4. Farming organically means making a number of commitments. Tick the statements which are true:

A Organic farmers try not to harm the environment.

B Organic farmers try not to harm wildlife.

C Organic farmers avoid using modern machinery including tractors.

D Organic farmers only grow crops – they are not allowed to farm animals. [1]

5. After 5 years of farming organically, Joe and Sarah notice that their yield is falling year by year. Here are some possible reasons why this is happening and ideas about what they could do. Choose the statement you think best applies.

A There was very little rain this year and they are not allowed to water the plants. They should choose a crop that needs less water.

B The soil now contains fewer nutrients. They need to add organic fertilisers or leave the field fallow for a year to recover.

C The seeds they sowed this year are substandard. They need to find a new source of seeds.

D This year's crop was eaten by pests. They will have to return to inorganic farming methods to get rid of them. [1]

## Sports science

**1** Kate is a physiologist at a local sports club. Her notebook contains the following data about Ravi, a young man who has just joined the club:

| | |
|---|---|
| Resting heart rate of ordinary male | 70 bpm |
| Ravi's resting heart rate | 60 bpm |
| Ravi's heart rate when he is running steadily | 140 bpm |
| Ravi's heart rate when he is sprinting fast | 160 bpm |

a What does 'bpm' stand for? [1]

b When she measures Ravi's resting heart rate, Kate draws a conclusion about Ravi's level of general fitness. What does she conclude and why? [3]

c Why does Ravi's heart rate increase when he begins running? In your answer, describe the changes that take place in the cardiovascular system. [3]

d During the fast sprinting session, Ravi's leg muscles begin to feel as if they are burning. What explanation can you give for this? [2]

e Describe and explain two other physiological changes that happen to the body when Ravi exercises hard. [4]

f Kate monitors Ravi's heart rate after the exercise session. What can these measurements tell her? [1]

**[Total 14 marks]**

**2** A material scientist asks a cycle team to try out two different fabrics for T-shirts. He gives two riders cotton shirts and two riders nylon shirts.

a Which of these is a natural material and what source does it come from? [2]

b Which of these is a synthetic material and what source does it come from? [2]

The cyclists report back that the cotton feels great at first but becomes wet with sweat and uncomfortable by the end of the ride. Meanwhile the nylon fabric seems to wick sweat away from the skin and stays cool and light.

c Explain what is happening when the cotton fibres encounter water and why they feel sodden and heavy. [2]

d Explain what is happening when the nylon fibres encounter water and how this enables the fabric to feel cool, dry and light. [3]

e Describe one other advantage of having a shirt made of nylon rather than cotton. [2]

**[Total 11 marks]**

**3** The coach of an ice-hockey team is explaining to his players the importance of having the right equipment. He shows them a helmet which has a protective face shield. He asks the team to think about the function of the face shield and what properties it requires.

a Set out three key properties a face shield should have. [3]

b Now suggest how suitable each of the following materials would be for this purpose.

i glass

ii natural soft rubber

iii aluminium

iv titanium

v iron

vi steel

vii fibreglass composite

viii oak [8]

**[Total 11 marks]**

**4** Jeff is a tennis player who is returning to his training program after a year of rest. He has spent the last year working as a radio presenter and website designer.

a Give the names of two muscles which will become stronger. [2]

b Give the name of two organs which will become more efficient and/or stronger. [2]

c Explain how you would expect Jeff's dietary needs to change, in terms of the number of calories he needs each day and why. [3]

During his training, Jeff regularly monitors his heart rate. He measures it:

- as soon as he wakes up
- before running on a treadmill
- while running on a treadmill
- at repeated intervals after running on a treadmill.

Jeff knows that the heart of an athlete can pump up to 50% more blood with each beat, compared with a normal heart.

**d** Which of these measurements most accurately tells Jeff his resting heart rate? [1]

**e** Which of these measurements can tell Jeff his recovery rate? [2]

**f** How does Jeff expect his resting heart rate to change as he gets fitter and why? [2]

Here is a plot of Jeff's heart rate during one of his first training sessions on a treadmill.

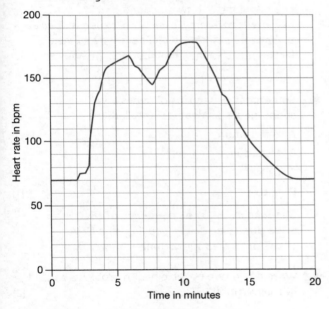

**g** What is the time on the graph that corresponds to Jeff turning the heartbeat monitor on? [1]

**h** What is the time on the graph that corresponds to Jeff beginning to run? [1]

**i** What is happening to Jeff's heartbeat 4 minutes into the run and what might explain this? [2]

**j** What is happening to Jeff's heartbeat 6 minutes into the run and what might explain this? [2]

**k** What is Jeff's heart rate just before he stops running? [1]

**l** What is Jeff's heart rate 1 minute after he finally stops running? [1]

**m** What is his heart rate 2 minutes after he stops running? [1]

**n** How many minutes does it take for Jeff's heart rate to return to normal after he stops running? [1]

**o** How does Jeff hope that this time will change as he gets fitter? [1]

**[Total 23 marks]**

# Model answers

**1** Which of the following describes the effect of oestrogen on the body?

A  Causes ovulation

B  Stimulates ovaries to produce FSH

C  Inhibits FSH production

D  Causes eggs to mature in the ovaries          [1]

FSH stimulates the ovaries to produce oestrogen, which operates in a negative feedback mechanism to prevent the pituitary releasing any more FSH to prevent another egg maturing. So, the answer is C.

**2** Which of the following health problems are linked to lack of food?

A  Obesity

B  Diabetes

C  Reduced resistance to infection

D  High blood pressure          [1]

When a person does not get enough food they cannot fight diseases, because their white blood cells cannot destroy bacteria and viruses. This leads to reduced resistance to infection. So, the answer is C.

**3** Which of the following statements about smoking is true?

A  Giving up smoking will not reduce the risk of dying from cancer.

B  Smoking relieves stress and so helps to lower blood pressure.

C  Passive smoking is harmless.

D  Pregnant women who smoke have smaller babies.          [1]

Tobacco smoke contains carbon monoxide, which means the blood cannot carry as much oxygen as it should. The developing baby does not get enough oxygen and cannot grow properly, so the answer is D.

**4** How many chromosomes are there in a human sperm cell?

A  46

B  26

C  43

D  23          [1]

A sperm cell contains just one copy of each chromosome. It fuses with an egg cell, which also contains one copy of each chromosome, to produce a zygote with pairs of each chromosome. The answer is D.

**5** Which two of the following are most likely to be causes of extinction?

A  New diseases

B  An earthquake

C  New predators

D  A hurricane          [1]

Whilst an earthquake and a hurricane may cause many deaths, there are still likely to be some survivors of each species to breed and maintain the population. New diseases and new predators may, over time, cause a species to become extinct as the balance between births and deaths changes. So, the answer is A and C.

**6** Sometimes new forms of genes arise spontaneously. What is this called?

A  Fertilisation

B  Mutation

C  Cancer

D  Mitosis          [1]

Changes in the base sequence of DNA may arise due to errors in 'copying' the DNA. These are called mutations (answer B).

**7** Write down two possible health problems caused by malnutrition.          [2]

Any two of the following would be accepted:
   Irregular periods in women.
   Reduced resistance to disease.
   Poor growth.
   Deficiency diseases, for example scurvy, rickets, night blindness.

**8** Explain why oestrogen can be used in oral contraceptive pills.          [3]

Oestrogen affects the pituitary gland, preventing it from releasing FSH. Without FSH, no eggs will mature inside the ovaries, so ovulation and pregnancy cannot occur.

**9** Describe two advantages and two disadvantages of oral contraceptives. [4]

Any two advantages from: women can control when they want to have families, fewer unwanted pregnancies, easy to use.

Any two disadvantages from: no protection against sexually transmitted infections, expensive, increase in promiscuity

## Chemistry C1a and C1b

**1** Match words **A**, **B**, **C** and **D** with the spaces in the sentences.

A magnesium carbonate B calcium oxide
C carbon dioxide D calcium carbonate

Limestone is a naturally occurring resource which contains the compound __1__. Limestone can be decomposed by heating it and it forms the gas __2__ and __3__ (quicklime). Carbonates of other metals such as __4__ decompose in the same way. [1]

Answers   1D   2C   3B   4A

**2** Match the processes **A**, **B**, **C** and **D** with the reactions they bring about in **1**, **2**, **3** and **4**.

A polymerisation          B thermal decomposition
C fractional distillation  D reduction

1 obtaining plastics from alkenes
2 obtaining iron from iron oxide
3 obtaining lime from limestone
4 obtaining petrol from crude oil [1]

Answers   1A   2D   3B   4C

In Q3–4 select the correct answer.

**3** Plant oils are an important source of energy in our diet.
1 They are extracted from nuts, seeds and fish.
2 They are needed in our diet as they provide the materials for growth and repair.
3 They don't mix with water but they can be made into emulsions.
4 They can be hardened into spreadable fats by reacting with nickel at 60 °C. [1]

1 is incorrect, fish are not plants!
2 is incorrect, oils give energy and vitamins.
3 is correct.
4 is incorrect. Oils are reacted with hydrogen. Nickel is the catalyst.

**4** Our atmosphere today has been much the same for the last 200 million years.
1 It contains about 80% oxygen.
2 It contains noble gases such as hydrogen and helium.
3 It contains 20% carbon dioxide and this percentage is increasing due to fossil fuel burning.
4 It contains about 20% oxygen almost none of which was present in the early atmosphere on Earth. [1]

1 is incorrect, nitrogen forms 80% of the air.
2 is incorrect, $H_2$ is not a noble gas.
3 is incorrect, only about 0.03% $CO_2$ is present.
4 is correct.

**5** The symbol equation for the decomposition of calcium carbonate is: $CaCO_3 \rightarrow CaO + CO_2$

a Explain how you know that this equation is balanced. [1]

There are the same number of each type of atom in the reactants and products.

b What does the formula $CaCO_3$ tell you? [1]

$CaCO_3$ contains one atom of calcium and one atom of carbon for every three oxygen atoms.

c Balance the equation below. [1]
___ Mg + ___ HCl → ___ $MgCl_2$ + ___ $H_2$

$Mg + 2HCl \rightarrow MgCl_2 + H_2$

**6** a Describe the structure of a metal such as pure copper and use this to explain how copper may be easily bent. [2]

The metal atoms are arranged in layers which can slide over each other.

b How does the addition of carbon to pure iron make the iron harder and stronger? [2]

Adding carbon atoms distorts the layers making it harder for them to slide over each other.

**7** The diagram below shows methane.

$$H-\overset{\displaystyle H}{\underset{\displaystyle H}{C}}-H$$

a Draw a molecule of a saturated hydrocarbon with two carbons. [2]

b Draw a molecule of an unsaturated hydrocarbon with two carbons. [2]

8 Noble gases are very unreactive but they still have many uses. Give examples of two different noble gases and state a use for each.

Gas 1 Neon     Use for gas 1: In discharge lamps [2]

Gas 2 Helium    Use for gas 2: In balloons [2]

## Physics P1a and P1b

1 Which of the following quantities is not a scalar?

A speed

B distance

C velocity

D time [1]

A scalar quantity has only magnitude; whereas a vector quantity has both magnitude and direction. In the list above, all quantities are scalar apart from velocity. Velocity is a vector quantity. Hence the answer is C.

2 Two cars X and Y are travelling on a road at the same constant speed. Car X has a greater mass than car Y. Which statement below is incorrect?

A Both cars have the same weight.

B Car X has greater momentum than car Y.

C Both cars have the same momentum.

D Both cars are accelerating. [1]

The weight of a car depends on its mass and acceleration due to gravity (weight = mg). Since the cars have different masses, they cannot have the same weight. Hence A is incorrect. Momentum is defined as:

$$momentum = mass \times velocity.$$

Since car X has a greater mass but the same speed, its momentum is definitely more than that of car Y. B is the correct answer.

C is incorrect because the cars do have different masses and D is also incorrect because the acceleration of each car is zero.

3 An electric heater of rating 2800 W is used to warm a small room in a house.

a What is the power of the heater in kilowatts? [1]

1 kW is equal to 1000 watts, therefore the power of the heater is 2.8 kW.

b Explain what is meant by the kilowatt hour. [2]

The kilowatt hour is the energy transformed when an appliance of power 1 kW is operated for a time of 1 hour.

c Calculate the cost of using this heater for a period of 24 hours given that the cost of each kWh is 14p. [5]

Number of kWh = power (kW) × time (hours)

Number of kWh = 2.8 × 24

Number of kWh = 67.2

Cost = number of kWh × cost per kWh

Cost = 67.2 × 14p

Cost = 940.8 p ≈ £9.41

4 Radio telescopes are used to image distant galaxies using microwaves.

a Write two things you know about microwaves. [2]

Microwaves are electromagnetic waves.

Microwaves travel through a vacuum at the speed of light (300 000 000 m/s).

b The microwave spectrum from all galaxies being observed show a red shift.

i What does 'red shift' mean? [1]

The entire spectrum from a galaxy is shifted to longer wavelengths.

ii What does red shift tell us about the Universe? [2]

Red shift implies that all galaxies are moving away from each other, and therefore the Universe is expanding.

## Forensic science

1 When compounds form, the bonding may be ionic or covalent. Sodium chloride is bonded ionically.

a What forces hold the sodium and chlorine together? [1]

Electrostatic attraction between oppositely charged ions.

b Are these forces strong or weak? [1]

Strong

c Would you expect the melting point of sodium chloride to be high or low? [1]

High

**2 a** Describe how you would test for the presence of ethanol and state what result you would obtain if the test was positive. [3]

*Warm with acidified potassium dichromate which turns from orange to green.*

**b** A second substance is heated with Benedict's solution and the blue solution forms a brick red precipitate. What substance was present in this sample? [1]

*Glucose*

**3** Match the methods below to the test they are used for by drawing lines to connect them.

| 1 | flame test | A | a bullet from a suspect and one from a crime scene |
| 2 | polarising microscope | B | carbonate ions |
| 3 | electron microscope | C | fine detail in tiny specks of paint |
| 4 | comparison microscope | D | looking at size and shape of grains in a soil sample |
| 5 | light microscope | E | stress patterns in plastics |
| 6 | addition of hydrochloric acid | F | metal ions |

[6]

*Answers   1F   2E   3C   4A   5D   6B*

**4** DNA is becoming more and more useful in solving crimes.

**a** Give two sources of DNA that may be obtained from a crime scene. [2]

*Any two from semen, saliva or blood.*

**b** DNA is cut into fragments using enzymes and these fragments are then subjected to a process called electrophoresis. Describe how this is used to produce a DNA profile. [6]

*Two electrodes of opposite charge are placed at different sides of a layer of electrophoresis gel. Negatively charged DNA fragments move to the positive electrode and positively charged fragments to the negative electrode. Fragments of different sizes and charge travel at different speeds and so they are separated.*

**5 a** Describe how you would find the refractive index of a glass block. [5]

*Pass a beam of light through the block. Mark the position of the block, the incident ray and the refracted ray. Draw a normal to the block at the point where it enters the block. Measure the angle of incidence and the angle of refraction using a protractor.*

**b** What is the equation used to calculate the refractive index of a material? [1]

$$\text{Refractive index} = \frac{\sin i}{\sin r}$$

## Food science

**1** A dietician has been asked to organise a healthy eating week at a local company. During the week, employees will be given leaflets about healthy eating and the cafeteria will offer healthier lunches.

**a** Which of these headlines would be most appropriate for the leaflet? [1]

  A Most Brits eat too little salt – are you among them?

  B A healthier diet can help you feel better and live longer!

  C The more you eat, the more you grow.

  D Stop eating the foods you like – they're bad for you.

*B*

The dietician gives the cook this menu for Monday's lunch.

| MENU | |
|---|---|
| Food A | A grilled pork chop |
| Food B | One cup of steamed broccoli florets |
| Food C | One jacket potato |
| Food D | A portion of polyunsaturated margarine |
| Food E | Fruit salad in natural juice |

The dietician explains this menu has a balance of protein, carbohydrates, fats and fibre.

**b** Which food item is the main source of protein? [1]

*A*

**c** Which food is the main source of carbohydrates? [1]

*C*

**d** List the three foods that supply fibre. [1]

B, C and E

**e** List the two foods that supply most of the fats. [1]

A and D

**f** The margarine has added vitamins A and D. Why were these vitamins chosen? [2]

Because they are fat soluble and margarine is a fat.

**g** The cook says she usually boils the vegetables in a pan of water and then drains them, but the dietician says the vegetables should be steamed instead. What is the problem with boiling and draining? [3]

Vitamin C moves into the water and is then drained away.

**h** One of the employees knows he has a very high cholesterol level. The dietician discovers he regularly has a pie and chips for lunch. Which of these suggestions might be particularly appropriate for him? [2]

　A Reduce the amount of sugar and starch in his diet.

　B Reduce the amount of salt and fat in his diet.

　C Drink more water – about eight glasses a day.

　D Eat fewer meals each day.

B

**2** A shopper buys a pot of dried pasta noodles and a tub of potato salad. Neither item contains preservatives.

The storage instructions on the noodles say, 'Keep in a cool dry place'.

The instructions on the potato salad say, 'Keep refrigerated. Eat within 2 days'.

**a** Why don't the noodles need to be put in the refrigerator? [2]

The noodles are dried. Bacteria won't grow on dried food.

One of the issues with this pot of noodles is that it is high in sodium. Here are the ingredients:

dried spaghetti, tomato powder, sugar, potato starch, vegetable oil, salt, flavour enhancer: monosodium glutamate, onion powder, carrot powder, colours: caramel, paprika extract

**b** Which ingredient or ingredients in this list are the major sources of sodium? [2]

Salt and monosodium glutamate

**c** Which of these groups of people are advised to be especially careful about their sodium intake? [1]

　A people with cavities

　B people with high blood pressure

　C people over the age of 50

　D women during menstruation

B

**d** A shopper forgets to put the potato salad in the fridge and finds it in a shopping bag in the hallway the next day. Is it safe to eat? Why or why not? [2]

No, because bacteria can grow in the warm hallway.

**3** An advertisement for a new fruit smoothie says it contains essential nutrients.

**a** What are essential nutrients, according to nutritionists? [2]

Essential nutrients are substances that the body needs and can only get from food. They can't be made in the body.

**b** Which two of these are not essential nutrients? [2]

　water　　vitamin D　　omega 6　　calorie

Vitamin D, calorie

**c** The product claims to be 'a good source of calcium'. Which of these ingredients is the source of calcium? [1]

strawberries　　melon　　milk　　ascorbic acid

Milk

**4** **a** What are antioxidants and why are they useful? [2]

Antioxidants are chemicals that help to stop foods from reacting with oxygen in the air. Without them, many foods deteriorate – oily foods taste rancid and vegetables lose colour.

**b** A slice of apple is put on a plate. At the same time, a second slice is coated in lemon juice and put on another plate. How would you expect these two slices of apple to change visibly over the next 10 minutes and why? [5]

The slice covered in lemon juice would stay fresh – there is vitamin C in lemon juice which is a natural antioxidant. The slice of apple that has no lemon juice is exposed to the air, so oxidisation will take place. The fruit will go brown.

c Selina has found that if she puts a thin coating of honey on sliced fruit, it helps the fruit to stay fresh longer. Why is this? [1]

Honey also contains antioxidants and will slow down the oxidisation process.

**5** a People with diabetes take insulin when they eat. What is the role of insulin in the body? [3]

It helps cells to take up glucose from the blood. It directs the muscle cells and liver to take up glucose from the blood and store it as glycogen.

b A person with diabetes injects insulin but eats only a small snack. A short time later she begins to shake and feel unwell. What might be happening? [2]

Her blood sugar level has fallen too low and there is not a sufficient glucose supply to her cells.

c Why do you think many people with diabetes carry a sugary snack with them? [1]

So that if their blood sugar level falls too low, they can eat the snack and push it back up.

## Sports science

**1** Footballer Steve Smith is returning to training after 6 months away with a serious injury. The team's physiologist, Jaya, welcomes him back and spends the first session taking some baseline measurements.

a What are baseline measurements and why are they important? [2]

Baseline measurements are taken before a training program in order to have a set of comparison points that can be used to monitor changes and improvements.

b List three things that Jaya would measure during the session. [3]

Any three from: heart rate when resting, heart rate when exercising, breathing rate when resting/exercising, lung capacity, glucose content of blood, lactic acid threshold, muscle strength.

Steve spends 15 minutes jogging on the treadmill. At the end, Jaya sees that the back and armpits of his shirt are wet and that his face is red. He asks what is going to happen next. Jaya tells him to take a break and suggests he has a drink of water or a sports drink.

c What change in Steve's blood circulation has caused his face to go red, and why has this change occurred? [5]

Capillaries near the surface of his skin have dilated, bringing blood to the surface. This has happened because he is hot and it is one of the ways in which his body can bring his temperature down. Once it is near the surface, blood can lose heat to the air.

d Why does Jaya suggest that Steve needs to get a drink? [1]

Steve has lost water (by exercising and sweating) and needs to replace it.

e Jaya suggests he should have water or a sports drink. What about a syrupy drink or a cola – would each of these be as good? Explain your answer. [4]

Neither would be a good idea. A drink containing syrup would take longer to digest and the water would not enter the circulatory system so quickly. Cola contains caffeine which is a diuretic – it would cause the body to lose more water.

**2** Which of these descriptions most closely describes the work of a sports physiologist? [1]

A A physiologist learns about how the body's systems and organs function and then helps the athlete achieve optimum fitness.

B A physiologist learns about human nutrition and advises the athlete on the best diet for his/her particular sport.

C A physiologist learns about the properties of materials and then designs sporting equipment and sportswear that can help the athlete in competition.

A

**3** Cricket bats are made from soft fibrous wood such as willow. Before they are used for the first time, the bats must be oiled and 'knocked-in' with a mallet. This is to ensure that the bat dents but does not crack when it hits a ball. It can take 4 hours to prepare a bat for its first game.

This preparation work would not be necessary if cricketers began using bats made of other materials. Baseball players can take advantage of bats made from aluminium alloys and modern composite materials.

a What is a composite? [1]

A composite material consists of two or more materials mixed together.

**b** Which of these are composites: plywood, fibreglass, brass, clay? [2]

Plywood and fibreglass

**c** Would a bat made from pure aluminium rather than an alloy be just as usable? Why or why not? [2]

No. Pure aluminium is soft and would absorb the energy of the ball rather than bounce the ball back.

**d** How is aluminium changed into aluminium alloy? [1]

Aluminium is mixed with a small amount of another material such as copper to make an alloy.

**e** The aluminium bat is hollow. Materials scientists have tested walls of different thicknesses. How would a thin-walled bat differ from a thick-walled bat? [3]

Compared with a thick-walled bat, a thinner-walled bat is lighter, springier and more likely to crack and break.

**f** Give three advantages that a cricket bat made of a composite would have over the traditional wooden bat. [3]

Any three of the following: it would be lighter, more weather-resistant, stronger, the stiffness can be tailored to give optimum performance.

**4** The formula used to calculate an individual's body mass index (BMI) is:

$$BMI = \frac{weight}{height^2}$$

A trainee nutritionist has these notes jotted on a page of her notebook:

| BMI | |
|---|---|
| 19 or below | |
| 20–25 | ☺ |
| 25–30 | |
| over 30 | |

**a** Fill in the table correctly, using these terms: overweight, healthy, obese, underweight. [1]

| BMI | |
|---|---|
| 19 or below | underweight |
| 20–25 | healthy |
| 25–30 | overweight |
| over 30 | obese |

**b** Mr M is a 40-year-old man who is 180 cm tall and weighs 75 kg. What is his BMI? [2]

23 (Remember, height needs to be in metres!)

**c** His next door neighbour, Mr K, is also 180 cm tall and his weight is 102 kg. What is his BMI? [2]

31.5

**d** One of these gentlemen owns a dog which he walks every day. He eats a healthy balanced diet and swims twice a week before work. Do you think this is Mr M or Mr K? [1]

Mr M

**e** Invent a lifestyle and diet for the other gentleman that would explain his BMI. [2]

Any diet and lifestyle that shows that Mr K does not take regular exercise and has an unhealthy diet (high in fat), which gives him more energy than he needs.

**f** Mr R, who lives on the other side of Mr M, is an instructor at the local gym. He works out everyday. He has a very muscular build and relatively little body fat. He calculates his BMI and discovers that it is above the healthy range. How can this be explained? [2]

Mr R is muscular. His extra muscle tissue has increased his weight. Also muscle tissue is heavier than fat so a small amount of extra muscle can have a significant effect on his BMI.

**g** Which of these statements is the most accurate portrayal of the current situation in Britain? [1]

A These days, many people have sedentary lifestyles and do not take part in regular exercise. This means that it is very easy to consume more calories than they need to meet their daily energy needs.

B These days more people are going to the gym to get exercise instead of exercising while doing an active job. It is not possible to burn enough calories in a session at a gym or pool to lose weight.

C These days vegetarian food tastes better than it did in the past. This means that more people are switching to vegetarian diets.

A

# Answers

## NOW TRY THIS ANSWERS

### IN CONTROL – pages 6 and 7
**a** Chemical, secreted, glands, bloodstream, target, slower, longer, water, sugar
**b** Oestrogen, oestrogen, FSH, LH, oestrogen
**c** False, true, false, false, false, true, false

### KEEPING HEALTHY – pages 8 and 9
**a** False, true, false, false, false
**b** Human cells, cells, pathogens, about 1000
**c** i Pathogens ii antibody iii antibiotic iv lymphocytes v phagocytes
**d** Ingest, digest/destroy, antibodies, antigens, quickly, symptoms

### REPRODUCTION AND GENES – pages 10 and 11
**a** Asexual, identical, parent, sexual, gametes, fertilisation, offspring, variation
**b** i Fertilisation ii Gamete iii DNA iv Nucleus v Chromosomes
**c** ii, v, iv, i, iii
**d** False, true, false, true, true, false

### EVOLUTION AND EXTINCTION – pages 12 and 13
**a** Features, behaviours, suited/adapted, environment, survive, reproduce
**b** True, true, false, false, false, true
**c** ii, iv, iii, i, v
**d** i, iii, iv

### OUR IMPACT ON THE ENVIRONMENT – pages 14 and 15
**a** Increasing, longer, farming, health, disease, building, agriculture, waste
**b** Air, water, water, air, air, land, land
**c** Greenhouse, heat, re-radiated, hotter, greenhouse, global warming, fossil fuels, deforestation
**d** Non-renewable, renewable, non-renewable, renewable, renewable, renewable, renewable

### ALL ABOUT ATOMS – pages 16 and 17
**a** i Atom ii Symbol iii Group iv Elements v Nucleus vi Electrons
**b** Co
**c** NO
**d** Balanced equations show that atoms are not lost or gained in chemical reactions
**e** +, $\rightarrow$, one, one, oxygen
**f** i T ii F – it has many uses iii F – glass is made using limestone iv F – quicklime is calcium oxide

### METALS FROM ORES – pages 18 and 19
**a** i Gold ii Iron iii Carbon iv Iron oxide v Ore
**b** 96, brittle, soft, alloy, stronger, corrode rust
**c** i Titanium ii bend iii bridges
**d** i T ii F – doesn't corrode iii F – too soft, not too hard iv T v F – there is lots of aluminium ore

### CRUDE OIL – pages 20 and 21
**a** Mixture, compounds, fractional distillation, boiling point

**b** i Compounds ii $C_nH_{2n+2}$ iii saturated iv $C_7H_{14}$
**c** 3, 5, 2, 1, 4
**d** $CO_2$ and $H_2O$, $SO_2$, $SO_2$, S, $H_2O$, $CO_2$, solid particles

### CRACKING AND POLYMERS – pages 22 and 23
**a** i Small hydrocarbons ii $C_nH_{2n}$ iii $C_7H_{14}$ iv Saturated

v

vi Small molecules
**b** Steam, catalyst, ethene, steam, plastics, poly(ethene), alkanes, fuels
**c** i Poly(ethene) ii Poly(propene) iii Poly(styrene) iv Poly(butene)
**d** i F – it is difficult to separate them ii T iii F – many make toxic fumes when burnt iv T

### FOOD CHEMISTRY – pages 24 and 25
**a** Energy, nutrients, mustard, emulsion, coat, texture
**b** Unsaturated: $C_3H_6$, decolourises bromine, contains at least one C=C double bond, general formula is $C_nH_{2n}$
Saturated: methane, iodine solution stays brown $C_3H_8$, contains only C-C single bonds
**c** i ACD ii BEF iii AD iv C

### THE EARTH AND ITS ATMOSPHERE – pages 26 and 27
**a** i Large piece of Earth's crust and upper mantle ii Provides energy for convection currents in the mantle iii A few metres every century iv Occur at plate boundaries v Has occurred since its formation
**b** i Nitrogen ii Oxygen iii Water vapour iv Carbon dioxide v Water vapour
**c** i Neon ii Neon or argon iii Helium
**d** DOWN, DOWN, UP, UP, DOWN, DOWN, DOWN, DOWN, UP

### THERMAL ENERGY – pages 28 and 29
**a** i, ii, iv
**b** i, ii
**c** i insulator ii Poor iii Close together

### EFFICIENT USE OF ENERGY – pages 30 and 31
**a** Kinetic, chemical, heat
**b** i Remains stationary ii Watts iii Joules iv Second
**c** i, ii

### ELECTRICITY – pages 32 and 33
**a** Electrical, light, hot, portable
**b** i, ii, iv
**c**

### GENERATING ELECTRICITY – pages 34 and 35
**a** Coil, magnet, voltmeter, wires
**b** Renewable: straw, manure
Non-renewable: coal, uranium, crude oil
**c** Electricity, uranium, water, steam
**d** i, iii

### ELECTROMAGNETIC WAVES – pages 36 and 37
**a** m/s, m, Hz
**b** iii, iv
**c** Ultraviolet waves, X-rays, gamma rays
**d** Radio waves, microwaves, infrared waves, visible light

### RADIOACTIVITY – pages 38 and 39
**a** ii, iii
**b** Tracer, pass, increase
**c**

### THE UNIVERSE – pages 40 and 41
**a** i, iv
**b** Moon, Mars, Sun, Pluto
**c** 2, 1, 3, 4
**d** Red shift, space is at −270 °C, galaxies are moving away from us

### EVIDENCE FROM MARKS AND IMPRESSIONS – pages 42 and 43
**a** bridge, carbon, aluminium, no-one
**b** 3, 2, 4, 6, 5, 1
**c** shoe brand, shoe size, height

### IDENTIFYING CHEMICALS – pages 44 and 45
**a** qualitative, melting, boiling, soluble, structure, bonding
**b** ionic, ions, 2+, electrostatic
**c** $CaCl_2$, $Na_2O$, $AlI_3$
**d** $C_6H_{12}O_6$, ethanol, strong, orange, brick red

### QUALITATIVE ANALYSIS OF IONIC COMPOUNDS – pages 46 and 47
**a** i $Ba^{2+}$; ii sodium ions; iii potassium ions; iv $Ca^{2+}$, $Li^+$, calcium ions
**b** $SO_4^{2-}$, $Ca^{2+}$, $Pb^{2+}$, $Fe^{3+}$
**c** hydrochloric acid, carbon dioxide, limewater, milky
**d** sodium nitrate + lead sulphate (ppt), sodium nitrate + silver chloride (ppt), potassium hydroxide + barium sulphate (ppt), sodium chloride + iron(II) hydroxide (ppt), potassium sulphate + copper(II) hydroxide (ppt)

### TOOLS FOR THE JOB – pages 48 and 49
**a** i comparison microscope ii electron microscope iii polarising microscope
**b** colour, texture, pattern, type
**c** 2, 3, 1, 7, 5, 6, 4
**d** scratched, same, comparison

## BLOOD TYPING – pages 50 and 51

**a** profiling, enzymes, electrophoresis, blood, semen, saliva, related
**b** veins, C, platelets, O
**c** F, B, A, C, E, D
**d** B, D, A, C, E

## PLASTIC AND GLASS – pages 52 and 53

**a** glass, refracted, refractive, index
**b**

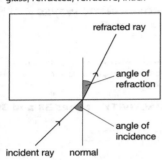

refracted ray

angle of refraction

angle of incidence

incident ray   normal

**c** E, D, C, B, A

## DATABASES – pages 54 and 55

**a** D, E, B, C, F, A
**b** does not, does not tell us, hair root, does not tell us
**c** composite, height, hair, clothes, hair, clothes

## HOW TO THINK LIKE A DIETICIAN – pages 56 and 57

**a** Low fat, high fibre diet
**b** We should eat five portions of fruit and/or vegetables each day
**d** A, D, E and K
**e** Heart, liver, kidneys – to protect them; skin – to insulate the body
**f** Hair, skin, muscle and bone
**g** **i** Fat **ii** Keeps skin and mucus linings healthy, protects body from infections, helps vision in dim light **iii** Night blindness, rough skin, prone to infections like colds, flu and pneumonia **iv** Cheese, eggs, oily fish, milk, yoghurt

## YOU ARE WHAT YOU EAT (AND DRINK) – pages 58 and 59

**a** 2100, 2500, 1900, 3500, 40-60
**b** proteins, digestion, build, hair
**c** glycogen, water, glycogen
**d** i, ii, iii, iv

## FATS, CHOLESTEROL AND SALT – pages 60 and 61

**a** fats, carbohydrates, fat, energy
**b** heart disease, 3 minutes, coronary artery, less saturated fat, angina
**c** saturated, saturated, cholesterol, unsaturated, cholesterol, avoided

## HOW TO THINK LIKE A FOOD SCIENTIST – pages 62 and 63

**a** **i** TEST 3 **ii** TEST 2 **iii** TEST 1
**b** no, fury, inedible, not
**c** low in calories, do not cause tooth decay
**d** It matters because you would be building up your intake by consuming a number of products.

## KEEPING FOOD SAFE – pages 64 and 65

**a** **i** = C and X **ii** = A and Y **iii** = B and Z
**b** Once
**c** Freezing, chilling, cooking, adding preservatives, drying
**d** To kill any bacteria on the loop
**e** i, ii, iii, iv, v, vi, vii

## FOOD AND FARMING – pages 66 and 67

**a** **i** bacteria **ii** fungus **iii** bacteria **iv** bacteria **v** yeast **vi** yeast
**b** **i** Artificial fertilisers **ii** Pesticides **iii** Herbicides
**c** organic, food, nutritional, agro-chemical, minimise, wildlife
**d** pesticide, flavouring, additive, bacteria, fertilise, preservative

## SPORTS SCIENCE BASICS – pages 68 and 69

**a** Cardiovascular system – physiologist; Isotonic sports drink – nutritionist; Aerodynamics – materials scientist; High protein diet – nutritionist
**b** Glucose sugar from food enters the bloodstream through the small intestine and binds to red blood cells; the blood takes it to muscle cells; the hormone insulin releases the glucose so that it moves into the muscle cells
**c** trachea, bronchi, alveoli
**d** glucose + oxygen → water + carbon dioxide + energy
**e** glucose → lactic acid + energy

## EXERCISE AND THE BODY – pages 70 and 71

**a** Capillaries are narrow tubes that carry blood
**b** If the body overheats, capillaries near the skin dilate to bring blood near the surface
**c** True
**d** Water moves into cells by osmosis and may cause them to burst
**e** Urine becomes more concentrated
**f** Insulin – pancreatic beta cells
**g** Glucagon – pancreatic alpha cells
**h** Beta, alpha and other hormone-producing cells cluster together in the pancreas to form 'islands'
**i** Tendons
**j** The hamstring
**k** The point where the tendon meets the bone we want to move

## PHYSIOLOGICAL CHANGES – pages 72 and 73

**a** observational, physiological, subjective, physiological
**b** A device used to measure lung capacity
**c** **i** maximum volume of gas that the lungs can hold **ii** volume of air breathed in or out during normal respiration
**d** A device used to measure grip
**e** Most people have a dominant hand with a stronger grip
**f** By testing athletes with a dynamometer regularly over a number of months to measure improvement
**g** endurance, athlete, diet, complex carbohydrates, glycogen, muscles

## NUTRITION – pages 74 and 75

**a** $BMI = \dfrac{\text{weight in kg}}{(\text{height in m})^2}$
**b** **i** underweight **ii** a healthy weight **iii** overweight
**c** The athlete's BER = 1.3 kcal × 50 × 24 = 1560 kcal
**d** The athlete's PER is 1560 + 800 = 2360 kcal
**e** energy, fat
**f** A kilocalorie is a unit of energy often used to describe food energy – 1 kc is 1000 calories; A joule is a metric unit of energy often used to describe electrical energy and sometimes food – 1 calorie = 4.184 J; 1 kcal = 4184 kJ
**g** Brown bread is high in carbohydrates and relatively low in fat
**h** Avocados are relatively high in fat and low in carbohydrates. Note that a gram of fat provides more energy than a gram of carbohydrate
**i** dehydration – B; sodium deficiency – C; low blood sugar – A

## MATERIALS FOR SPORT – pages 76 and 77

**a** clothes, footwear, sports surfaces, equipment
**b** It draws sweat away from the body and moves it to the surface of the skin where it can evaporate and cool the athlete
**c** hardwood – i; leather – ii; nylon – iii
**d** nylon, perspiration, mesh, perspiration, outdoor, wind-resistant

## METALS AND COMPOSITES – pages 78 and 79

**a** Ferrous metals contain iron, for example, iron and stainless steel
**b** Wood
**c** Hollow steel or titanium
**d** Composites – plywood, fibreglass, carbon-carbon; alloys – brass, pewter, steel
**e** low densities; track athletes; smoother surfaces; cyclists, swimmers and bobsledders; good thermal insulation; mountain climbers and deep-sea divers

## ANSWERS TO EXAM–STYLE QUESTIONS

### Biology B1a and B1b

**1** 1A, 2D, 3B, 4C
**2** 1C, 2A, 3B, 4D
**3** 1D, 2C, 3B, 4A,
**4** B
**5** 1C, 2A, 3B, 4D
**6** Slows reaction time, impairs judgement, blurred vision, slower to respond to hazards, increased sense of confidence
**7** Trees not photosynthesising, less carbon dioxide taken in, burning/decomposition of trees releases carbon dioxide, increased carbon dioxide causes increased greenhouse effect/global warming

**8** Unsightly/visual pollution, air pollution from increased traffic due to transportation of limestone, noise pollution from traffic, noise pollution from quarry, e.g. explosives used

## Chemistry C1a and C1b

**1** 1B, 2C, 3D, 4A
**2** 1B, 2D, 3A, 4C
**3** A
**4** B
**5** B
**6 a** An ore is a rock that contains enough metal to make it economic to extract it
  **b** Advantage: it provides employment
  Disadvantages: it may be noisy/can create a lot of extra road traffic/may create a lot of dust
**7 a** Make it brittle
  **b** An alloy is a mixture of metals (or a metal and carbon in the case of steel)
  **c** High carbon steel is very strong
**8 a** Any two from: to preserve/improve flavour/improve appearance
  **b** Crush the peas and extract the green colouring using a solvent; draw a line across the base of a strip of filter paper and add a spot of the green solution and a spot of tartrazine onto the line; place the filter paper into some solvent in a beaker; allow the solvent to creep up the filter paper and see if there is a spot at the same level as the tartrazine

## Physics P1a and P1b

**1** 1C, 2D, 3A, 4B
**2 a** D
  **b** C
**3 a** D
  **b** A
**4 a** B
  **b** C
**5 a** Some of the energy is lost as heat due to friction
  **b** 48 %
**6 a** Difference: gamma rays have a shorter wavelength (or higher frequency) than X-rays;
  Similarity: both are transverse waves
  **b** The half-life of an isotope is the average time for half of the nuclei to decay
  **c** Several gamma ray sources are pointed towards the cancerous cells in the patient; the energy of the gamma rays destroys the cancerous cells

## Forensic science

**1 a** Any two from: wear protective overalls; masks; gloves; hairnets
  **b** One from: placing tapes around the area; stationing a police officer to prevent access
**2** The area is first dusted with black carbon powder; the print is lifted with adhesive tape, placed onto card and labelled
**3 a** Any three from: sole patterns, brand of shoe, size of the shoe, wear marks
  **b** Height – because height and shoe size are proportional, the height of the wearer can also be estimated

**4** $C_2H_5OH$ — glucose
  $CO_2$ — water
  $H_2O$ — ethanol
  $C_6H_{12}O_6$ — carbon dioxide

**5**

| Results of test | Ion present |
|---|---|
| gives a lilac flame | Potassium $K^+$ |
| forms a rusty brown precipitate when sodium hydroxide solution is added | Iron(III) $Fe^{3+}$ |
| forms a blue precipitate when sodium hydroxide solution is added | Copper(II) $Cu^{2+}$ |
| forms a white precipitate when first nitric acid, then silver nitrate is added | Chloride $Cl^-$ |
| forms a white precipitate when first hydrochloric acid, then barium chloride solution is added | Sulfate $SO_4^{2-}$ |
| fizzes vigorously when dilute hydrochloric acid is added | Carbonate $CO_3^{2-}$ (a metal such as Mg or Zn would also be correct) |

**6 a** The fragment is placed in some oil and the oil is heated
  The refractive index of the oil at different temperatures is known
  When the oil's refractive index becomes the same as that of the glass, the fragment disappears from view
  A table is used to find the refractive index of the oil at this temperature; this is the RI of the glass
  **b** Whether the blood is from a human or an animal; a person's blood group; DNA can be extracted from it

## Food science

**1 a** fibre
  **b** calcium
  **c** salt
  **d** calcium
  **e** He needed additional energy to do the physical activity required to sail the boat
  **f** Vitamin C
  **g** It helps the immune system fight infection; builds healthy gums and keeps blood vessels strong
  **h** To store it – so it would not decay
  **i** Water
  **j** Yes – he has a balance of protein, carbohydrates, fibre and fats
**2 a** Table sugar provides energy but no other useful nutrients
  **b** Vitamin C, fibre, carbohydrates and fruit sugar (only two of these required)
  **c** Glucose which is also called blood sugar is the body's natural energy source; it is needed by all our cells for respiration to release energy and thus work muscles, fuel the brain, etc.
  **d** Fructose is a simple sugar – like glucose – and can enter the blood stream relatively quickly; while glucose is used for the body's immediate energy needs, fructose is taken to the liver and stored as glycogen (it is eventually released as glucose)

**e** Yes – because you can get the energy you need from other sources, such as other forms of sugar, complex carbohydrates and fats
**f** Insulin is released by the pancreas and this helps cells to take in glucose for respiration; insulin also triggers the liver cells to take in excess glucose and store it as glycogen
**3** A, C, D and E
**4** A and B
**5** B

## Sports science

**1 a** Beats per minute
  **b** Ravi is fit; his resting heart rate is lower than average which means it is a trained (fit) heart
  **c** When Ravi runs, his muscles respire, using oxygen and glucose and these need to be replaced; Ravi breathes faster to get more oxygen into his body; his heart rate increases so that his blood can carry oxygen to the muscles quickly; carbon dioxide (produced during respiration) is removed and returned to the lungs
  **d** If all the available oxygen has been used in respiration, the muscle cells respire anaerobically, releasing lactic acid
  **e** Any two from: Ravi feels hotter – heat is released by muscles; he pants – to get oxygen into his body more quickly and carbon dioxide out; he sweats – in attempt to keep his body temperature down
  **f** They indicate Ravi's recovery time – which is another indication of his level of fitness
**2 a** Cotton from a cotton plant
  **b** Nylon from petroleum
  **c** Cotton fibres absorb water and hence feel sodden and heavy
  **d** The nylon fibres do not absorb water, instead they channel it (it's called wicking) from the skin to the outer surface where the water evaporates and cools the athlete
  **e** Nylon is more durable (and it can be brightly coloured)
**3 a** Three from: strong (not brittle or breakable), rigid not rubbery, can be shaped (malleable), as light as possible
  **b i** glass (no – it would shatter)
   **ii** natural soft rubber (no – it would bend and allow the ball to hit the face)
   **iii** aluminium (yes, if it can be made strong enough)
   **iv** titanium (yes)
   **v** iron (no – it is too soft)
   **vi** steel (yes, if it is made strong enough)
   **vii** fibreglass composite (yes – this material is sometimes used to make a mask which covers most of the face)
   **viii** oak (no – hard to shape and would block too much vision)

**4**

**a** For example: biceps, triceps, quadriceps, hamstrings

**b** Heart and lungs

**c** Jeff needs more calories because he will use them to exercise for training and competition; a typical man needs about 2000 – Jeff may need another 2000 per day or more depending on the level of training

**d** The measurement taken as soon as he wakes up

**e** While running on treadmill and at repeated intervals afterwards (he also needs to note the time at which each measurement was taken)

**f** He expects his resting heart rate to go down; a fit heart can pump more blood with each beat than an unhealthy heart, hence the resting rate falls

**g** 0 minutes

**h** 2 minutes

**i** Jeff's heart rate slows down – he is probably taking a break or has jumped off the treadmill

**j** Jeff's heart rate speeds up – he is probably back on the treadmill, running again

**k** 178 beats per minute (175–180 is acceptable)

**l** 160 beats per minute

**m** 140 beats per minute

**n** 7 minutes (any answer in the range 7–8 minutes is acceptable)

**o** Jeff hopes that this recovery time will become shorter